As an active member ~~of~~ Society at the age of ei........ was firmly established .... keen New Zealand sportswoman, she discovered and used many natural healing preparations to treat her injuries long before they became fashionable.

After studying nursing and chemistry, Kay's travels gave her the opportunity to work as a nurse in several countries including setting up and running a small hospital on the Mediterranean. Fate then decreed a move to England, and the next few years were spent as a bodywork practitioner. Now, drawing on her unique background of sport, medicine and strong intuitive skills, Kay has begun her own business. She revels in creating her own sensual and practical range of essential oils.

AROUSING AROMAS

KAY COOPER

ORION

An Orion Paperback
First published in Great Britain in 1998 by
Orion Books Ltd,
Orion House, 5 Upper St Martin's Lane,
London WC2H 9EA

A CIP catalogue record for this book
is available from the British Library.

ISBN: 0 75281 546 6

Printed and bound in Great Britain by
The Guernsey Press Co. Ltd, Guernsey

The author of this book is not a physician, and the ideas, procedures
and suggestions in this book are intended to supplement, not replace,
the medical advice of trained professionals. Consult your medical
practitioner about any condition that may require diagnosis or medical
attention, and before adopting the suggestions in this book.

CONTENTS

INTRODUCTION

This little book is not meant to be an encyclopedia. Its aim is to bridge a gap. There are several excellent, but mostly expensive, aromatherapy reference books on the market, but for those who are beginners or want to use aromatherapy oils occasionally, where do you start? Try here. I have tried to provide a comprehensive, yet brief, background to the subject, followed by sections covering different ways essential oils relate to everyday life. Read a section or two before giving up. At the very least you'll know what all this aromatherapy babbling is about, and you may even decide to try a recipe or two! Just be careful – you might enjoy it!

PART ONE

What is Aromatherapy?

SMELL - THE ESSENTIAL SENSE

Some of us are aware of smells and their effects. Not one of us goes untouched by them. Smell seems to have a more direct link with our subconscious minds than any of our other senses. A smell can instantly trigger memories and enables us to recall the emotions associated with them. It is a powerful evocative sense.

Compared to our other senses, we make little conscious use of our sense of smell. Over the past two decades we have redis-covered a love of food and become much more aware of 'taste'. Consequently our sense of 'taste' has become much more sophisticated. Over the next fifty years I believe our sense of smell will become more important and in-depth research into the ways this sense affects us is already under way.

The word 'aromatherapy' derives from Greek, meaning 'treat-ment through smell' or fragrance. Aromatherapy is so accessible, it is a great medium through which we can become aware of, and utilize, our amazing sense of smell. It is a beautiful way to discover aspects of yourself and a natural ally in the continual search for balance in our chaotic world.

REDISCOVERING AROMATHERAPY

Aromatherapy is the name given to the use of naturally occur-ring oils to improve physical, mental and emotional well-being. But it is not new. We are only beginning to explore and practise what many cultures before us have utilized to the full. The following quote from the *New Scientist* summarizes this rather well, I think:

'I have an earache . . .'
2000BC   '*Here, eat this root.*'
AD1000 '*That root is heathen. Here, say this prayer.*'
AD1850 '*That prayer is superstition. Here, drink this potion.*'
AD1940 '*That potion is snake oil. Here, swallow this pill.*'
AD1985 '*That pill is ineffective. Here, take this antibiotic.*'
AD2000 '*That antibiotic is unnatural. Here, eat this root.*'

Although for centuries the healing powers of plants have been widely used, the term 'aromatherapy' was adopted by the French chemist, René Gattefossé, in 1928. When he badly burned his hand, he plunged it into the nearest liquid, a barrel of lavender oil. The healing of his hand was quite remarkable. It was this incident that led him to research, document and develop aromatherapy as we know it today.

ESSENTIAL OILS

These naturally occurring oils are extracted from roots, rinds, stalks, seeds, resin, nuts, bark, fruits, grasses, leaves and flowers of many different plants and trees. The resulting concentrated liquids are called essential oils.

These precious oils each have their own therapeutic properties. They are organic compounds, sometimes comprised of up to 500 different chemical constituents. The main active chemical groups are phenols, alcohols, esters, ketones, aldehydes and terpenes. Although many individual chemicals from plants are synthesized, or copied, in the laboratory, when used in their natural form there are far fewer negative side-effects. It seems that even in the tiniest amounts, the combination of chemicals occurring naturally in plants work 'together' in a way that an individually synthesized chemical cannot.

Whether you are aware of it or not, these oils operate on an

> It *seems that even in the tiniest amounts, the combination of chemicals occurring naturally in plants work 'together' in a way that an individually synthesized chemical cannot.*

emotional, intellectual and spiritual level, as well as on the cellular and physical. They *are* 'holistic' – they require nothing else to make them that way.

The plants essential oils derive from are seasonal crops. They vary each year according to climate and other changes in their growing environment – like wine, some years are better than others. Many different factors may affect the quality of an oil, such as altitude, soil and harvesting – that is, how long the raw material is grown and stored before the oil is extracted, and the method of extraction. These all alter the therapeutic value of the oils we use. Many importers and retailers do not appear to take the trouble to check these factors. It is important to find a supplier who knows where his oils come from and, if possible, a little about how they are cared for before they reach you.

Essential oils are not only used in medicine but also by the food and cosmetics industries. For example:

- Many essential oils are present in our prescribed drugs. Sometimes the molecular structure of an oil is synthesized and then used in a drug.
- In food and drink essential oils are used for natural flavour and aroma and also as preservatives.
- Cosmetic manufacturers include the cell-rejuvenating and skin-toning properties of oils in many cosmetics and skin preparations.
- Perfume houses are more concerned with the aroma, and sometimes mood- and emotion-enhancing qualities, of the oils.

HOW DO ESSENTIAL OILS WORK?

The most straightforward way to practise aromatherapy is by inhaling an essential oil. Each active ingredient, or chemical, in an essential oil has molecules of a specific shape. These find their matching 'jigsaw piece' in the membrane of the olfactory, or smell, system. When the matching 'jigsaw pieces' fit perfectly, a gateway opens for the chemical to be transmitted to the part of the brain called the limbic system. This area is concerned with emotion, attention, memory and learning. The limbic system responds to this chemical 'message' by releasing its own messages – its reply. It may send messages to uplift, calm down, balance the emotions, or even produce more white blood cells – the cells that are needed to fight off infection.

Synthetic drugs are developed to fight only one type of organism on behalf of our body. For this reason we can become dependent on a drug and it is very easy for the organisms to quickly evolve different strains for every drug we invent. Essential oils, on the other hand, stimulate and support the body to carry out the work itself. This actually serves to strengthen the immune system. Essential oils restore balance and are sensitive to body chemistry. They work *with* the body.

Once their job is done, essential oils will leave the body through the pores of the skin, by exhalation, or, like many waste products, are processed by the kidneys and become urine.

I never stop finding new aspects to essential oils. They constantly amaze me. In my work with oils I delight in seeing the power of natural drugs working. I was trained to work holistically – treat the whole person, body, mind and spirit – in nursing. But with aromatherapy there is no other way to work *but* holistically – you cannot prevent the emotional effect of an oil working even though you may have chosen it for its physical properties alone. This is where trained practitioners of aromatherapy are important. They have learnt how to combine oils in such a way that they care for all aspects of the person.

I find essential oils are so beautifully non-invasive, they will work in chemical harmony with the body without altering cellular

heat or electromagnetism. Administering them is such a pleasure, whether it is through massage, bathing or inhalation. They
are extremely efficient in the way the body absorbs them, as
opposed to drugs that are taken orally – probably the least
effective method of absorption. Perhaps that is why so many
nurses decide to study aromatherapy.

METHODS OF EXTRACTION

These are some of the main methods of extracting essential oils.

Solvent extraction. This produces some of the finest flower
absolutes. In aromatherapy this mainly concerns rose, neroli
and jasmine.

Using liquid butane or liquid carbon dioxide. This modern
extraction process can produce very fine oils without damaging
the most delicate aromas. Absolutes differ from essential oils –
those oils extracted by steam distillation – in that they have an
extremely strong perfume and therapeutic power and need to
be use in very low concentration.

Expression. Citrus fruits are extracted by simple pressure.
The peel – without any pith or pulp – is squeezed and aromatic
oil and juice is pressed out. The liquid is left to stand until the
oil and juice have separated out.

Distillation. The plant material is heated by one of two methods. In
the first method, called direct distillation, the material is immersed
in water which is then brought to the boil. The second method,
steam distillation, works by heating water below the material, which
is placed on a rack or grill, so that steam passes up through it.

CHOOSING YOUR OILS

It takes a great deal of work to produce all essential oils, but
some oils require huge quantities of the flower or plant to make
just one drop, or are extracted from a precious or rare source.

> *Each jasmine blossom must be hand picked before dawn, when the flower is only a day old, as that is when the concentration of oil in the petals is highest.*

For example, it takes two tons of fresh rose petals to create just one kilogram of rose oil. Consequently, this is one of the most expensive oils in general usage. Each jasmine blossom must be hand picked before dawn, when the flower is only a day old, as that is when the concentration of oil in the petals is highest. Sandalwood is taken only from the heartwood of a tree forty years old or more. No wonder these oils cost more than, say, lavender – three kilograms of essential oil can be produced from only 100 kilograms of the lavender plant. The cost of each oil should always reflect the cost of procuring it.

It is important to take care where and from whom you buy your oils. You want to know as far as possible that the oils you are investing in are full potency, have been cared for correctly and are not diluted – which is unfortunately more and more common due to the popularity of aromatherapy. Sometimes I wince when I hear people say, 'I bought this oil and it didn't work – aromatherapy doesn't work'. I always wonder about the quality of the oil they used and the instructions they were given.

When choosing your oils be mindful of the following things and let your intuition out for a data-gathering session.

- All essential oils should come in blue or amber bottles.
- When blended they should also be stored in these.
- Train your nose to smell natural oils.
- It takes at least a year to fully train your nose, so get to know the pattern of pricing. This will probably change over the years due to supply and demand, but generally the more difficult the extraction, the more costly the oil. Jasmine, rose

and neroli should always be significantly higher in price. Sandalwood and frankincense, ylang-ylang and clary sage should also cost at least two to three times more than lavender or citrus oils.

- Supplier reputation is not necessarily everything to go on. Advertising can be persuasive and misleading.
- Talk to your suppliers to get a sense of their product.
- Try and obtain good information on the oils from your suppliers.

STORING YOUR OILS

- Keep your essential oils and blends in amber or blue bottles as they are affected by ultraviolet light.
- Keep away from light, heat and damp.
- Keep the tops on tightly. Try not to get tops with eye droppers. Oils will evaporate through these droppers and the rubber will perish, sometimes into your oil.

FUNDAMENTALS

Get your fundamentals right – choose good oils, find good information on them and care for them properly. Then have fun with them. They are beautiful, natural tools for a more balanced daily life.

TAKING CARE

Oils are highly concentrated chemicals, with complex structures. They are powerful so use them with care. If used too frequently, or at the wrong time, they can do more harm than good.

1. Only use the following oils in moderation (a few days at a time)

basil	bay	camphor
cedarwood	cinnamon leaf	eucalyptus
fennel	ginger	hyssop
nutmeg	thyme	valerian

2. Phototoxic oils – do not use before spending time in the sun

angelica	bergamot	citronella
ginger	lemon	lime
mandarin		

3. Not to be used in pregnancy. It is a good rule not to use any essential oils in pregnancy unless you are under the care of an experienced aromatherapist.

angelica	basil	birch
cedarwood	citronella	clary sage
cypress	fennel	geranium
hyssop	jasmine	juniper
marjoram	myrrh	nutmeg
peppermint	rosemary	thyme
tarragon	yarrow	

4. These oils can irritate the skin – so dilute them *very* well before use

angelica	black pepper	cinnamon leaf
clove	ginger	lemon
lemongrass	lemon verbena	nutmeg
orange	peppermint	

5. Do not use these oils with epilepsy

| fennel | hyssop | rosemary |

6. Children
Do not use the oils listed in category 1. Apart from these, use essential oils as you would for adults but at about half strength. With inhalations always supervise a child and try them for about one minute initially. If they are OK then continue the inhalation. NEVER TRY TO TREAT SERIOUS PROBLEMS WITHOUT QUALIFIED MEDICAL HELP.

WAYS TO USE ESSENTIAL OILS

Essential oils can be used in a great many ways. These are the most popular.

ROOM FRAGRANCING

Human beings have been fascinated by fragrance in some form or other since time began. Now that our obsession with the 'synthetic' is waning, more and more people are discovering how lovely it is to fragrance their homes naturally. What a wonderful job it would have

> *Human beings have been fascinated by fragrance in some form or other since time began.*

been to be the maid in charge of the still room in the seventeenth century. You would have taken care of the herb garden and orchard, making sure plants were harvested at the correct time, in keeping with the phases of the moon and accompanied by the correct ceremonies. Using your knowledge of herbs, you would have provided all the household remedies, prepared aromatic vinegars, syrups, conserves and candies. Your pot pourri would have scented bedrooms, sitting-rooms and privies and your natural beauty lotions and waters would have been used by the ladies of the house. You would have made posies of herbs and flowers for your lord and lady to carry in the street to protect them from infectious diseases and awful smells. The use of fragrance in these many ways captures the imagination and is the sort of practical, natural fragrancing we are beginning to adopt once again.

Methods of using essential oils in your rooms are:

Pot Pourri. Use your older oils to boost your pot pourri. It is best to seal the pot pourri in a bag for forty-eight hours to allow the oils to permeate before reusing.

Candles. It is actually quite difficult to get good aromatherapy candles. Keep the wick trimmed quite low to retain the fragrance. Or you could try dropping three to four drops of oil into the warm wax near the lit wick of an ordinary candle. Do take great care as essential oils are all highly flammable.

Cotton balls. This is an easy way to fragrance any room in the colder months. Drop your oils on a cotton wool ball and sit it on a radiator. Try up to about six drops of oil.

Light bulbs. Ceramic or metal rings are available which rest over the bulb of an ordinary light fitting. Put a drop or two of oil in the ring and sit it on the light bulb. Always put the ring on before the bulb heats up. I find that a couple of drops of water helps the oil to disperse into the room, but be very careful not to spill either the oil or the water.

Room sprays. A plant spray bottle makes a good room spray. It is a good idea to dedicate just one plant sprayer to your oils. Use about five drops to every 200ml and shake well before spraying. Hold the spray about six to eight inches away and direct it towards carpets, curtains and cushions which will hold the aroma. Avoid aiming at woodwork and delicate fabrics.

Diffusers. These gently heat the oils so that they evaporate into the air. Ensure that the dish that holds the oils is not porous and always clean it while it is still warm. Oil burners either require a candle or are electrically operated. Flame-free or non-candle varieties of these diffusers are being introduced and may prove handy for the office, workroom or study. All kinds of diffusers can be beneficial to asthma and hayfever sufferers. They are also good insect repellents and handy for getting rid of unpleasant smells.

Water bowls. Pour boiling water into a bowl and drop in the essential oils of your choice. Close the doors and windows for a few minutes and the aroma will fill the room. Great for promoting sleep and when someone is ill.

ESSENTIAL OILS IN WATER

Baths. To my mind, adding oils to a bath is one of the great pleasures in life and a lovely way to enjoy them. The oils work through inhalation of the vapours and absorption of a small amount of oil through the skin. After running your bath (make sure the water is not too hot) add six to eight drops of any combination of oils. Swish the oils around before you soak for at least ten minutes. For those with sensitive skin and for children, it is a good idea to use only three to four drops of oil blended with a little carrier oil before putting them in the bath.

Foot baths. The great 'mini-pamperer' is the foot bath. It will affect all of you, not just your feet, so choose your oils with care. Fill your bowl with warm water first before adding up to six drops of essential oil. Soak for at least ten minutes – longer if you can.

Hand baths. As for foot baths, but hand baths will usually require less water, so try just four drops of essential oil. Hand baths are great for wounds, muscle injuries and arthritis.

Sitz baths. This is a hip-level bath in either a bath or a bowl big enough to sit in. Always run the water first, then add only two to three drops of essential oil and make sure they are well dispersed in the water before sitting in it.

Showers. I didn't think essential oils could be used effectively in the shower until a friend of mine, who loves her showers, convinced me they do. Try washing as usual, then add about six drops of essential oil to your flannel and give yourself a good rub down while still under the running water. You could also rub yourself down with a ready-mixed oil – using it like a body oil – after your shower. Remember to inhale as you go so you make the most of the oils.

INHALING ESSENTIAL OILS

Tissue. One of the simplest ways to utilize essential oils is to put a couple of drops on a tissue and inhale the aroma. This method can be used for getting to sleep, waking up, travel sickness, as a pick-me-up, for headaches, to help concentration when writing and studying and it can even ease hangovers!

Classic Inhalation. Pour boiling water into a bowl and add about six drops of any combination of essential oils. Lean over the bowl and cover your head with a towel. Close your eyes and inhale deeply. Try and do this for about two minutes, then take a break and lift the towel. Repeat several times. This is also an alternative method of cleansing the skin.

ESSENTIAL OILS FOR THE SKIN

Compress. To a small amount of water in a basin, add up to six drops of essential oil. Mix the oil well into the water. Place a flannel in the water and then gently wring it out and apply to the affected area. Cover with a bandage or towel. When the compress is at body temperature, repeat the process.

A cold compress is used for headaches, arthritis and inflamed and swollen joints. A hot compress is good for backaches, menstrual discomfort, earache or toothache.

Direct. This is not a usual way to use essential oils but can be very effective. You can apply neat lavender to just-burned skin, or a drop of tea tree oil to an insect bite. Always be careful when using oils neat on the skin. Apply them with a cotton bud to target the affected area.

Massage. The smoothing of any oil over the skin in a rhythmical manner is relaxing. By using essential oils in the massage oil we can help the body to greater balance and health. Add one drop of essential oil to every 2ml of carrier or base oil (see below). Only mix about 20ml of oil at a time and keep whatever you have left over in a brown bottle with a screw top (most pharmacies sell these).

Massage will stimulate the circulation of blood and lymph. It can relieve tension, aches and pains and help the elimination of toxins. At the same time, it will help improve the tone and elasticity of the skin. Before you have a massage, have a bath or shower. This begins the relaxation process, and, as it may take up to six hours for the oils to be absorbed, is preferable to a shower or bath afterwards. Always make sure that the massage room is warm and that the oil is warmed in the palm of the hand before applying to the skin.

CARRIER OILS

Essential oils are concentrated and very powerful. When they are used on the skin they must be diluted. With the exception of lavender and tea tree this applies to every essential oil. The carrier oil or base oil provides lubrication in massage and is the perfect medium with which to dilute essential oils.

> *Essential oils are concentrated and very powerful. When they are used on the skin they must be diluted.*

A carrier or base oil may be almost any vegetable oil. A mineral oil – such as baby oil – will always remain on the surface of the skin. A vegetable oil will be absorbed into the skin taking the essential oils through the layers of the skin into the body. It 'carries' the essential oils into the system.

The process of adding essential oils to a carrier oil is called blending. A standard blend (three per cent) will contain ten drops of essential oil to 20ml of carrier oil. This is considered a therapeutic level of oils – the level at which the properties of essential oils will be effective.

Most aromatherapists use sweet almond and grapeseed oil for general massage work and add five to ten per cent of wheatgerm oil if a blend needs to be kept for a while. Wheatgerm contains a very high percentage of vitamin E which will naturally help to preserve an oil. All oils 'oxidize' when exposed to the air. This means that over a period of time the exposure to air will turn them rancid. The wheatgerm will slow this process down and help to keep the oil longer. For this reason, it is a good idea to blend your oils only as you need them or for a month or two at a time.

Most essential oil suppliers and healthfood shops stock carrier oils. It is always nice to use the best oils. Try to find cold-pressed oils containing no additives of any description.

An entire carrier oil may be one or a mixture of these: sweet almond, apricot kernel, peach kernel, corn, grapeseed, hazelnut, peanut, safflower, soya bean and sunflower.

The following oils are also carrier oils but are best used as only a part – say about ten per cent – of the total carrier oil: wheatgerm, sesame, olive, jojoba, carrot, evening primrose, borage seed, avocado.

Carrier oils are a subject in their own right as they all have their own individual properties. I have covered those that I consider most useful in the different sections of this book.

TWO KEY ESSENTIAL OILS: LAVENDER AND TEA TREE

These two indispensable essential oils are worth their weight in gold. Even if you are not interested in oils, these are a *must* for the home.

LAVENDER

Lavender is a magical oil. It promotes relaxing, restful sleep and is a natural remedy for minor burns, scratches, grazes to the skin, even spots. In this one special oil you also find a natural, aro-

> *Lavender will gently and naturally stimulate your immune system*

matic and effective potion for all types of headaches. And, in addition, lavender will gently and naturally stimulate your immune system.

When I first began working with oils, lavender was not my favourite. I appreciated that it was probably the most versatile of essential oils – it is one of the mildest, yet most effective oils, and has a wide range of therapeutic properties. Now I appreciate its beauty and truly love the aroma. I cannot remember life before lavender.

Whenever anyone asks where to begin with essential oils, my reply is always: lavender. Use it, smell it, look at the plant, get to know the 'lavender personality'. When I think of lavender, I think 'restoring'. Restoring balance is what lavender does best, in mind or body – it will attempt to balance you – whatever state you're in. Sometimes it may relax, sometimes it may uplift, but it always works towards balance.

The history

Lavender derives its name from the Latin *lavare*, meaning 'to wash' and has been used throughout history. The ancient Romans added it to their baths as a cleanser. Ancient Greeks, Romans and Persians all burned lavender in sick rooms and to fumigate their houses against epidemics. In 1633, John Gerarde wrote in his herbal: 'the distilled water of lavender smelt unto, or the temples and forehead bathed therwith, is refreshing to them that have the Catalepsie, a light Migrain and to them that have the falling sickness and the use to swoon to much'. John Parkinson, whose herbal dates from the same time, also noted that a mixture of the husks and flowers of lavender would 'openth the stoppings of the liver, the lungs, the milt, the mother, the bladder and in one word all other inward parts, cleansing and driving forth all evil and corrupt humours'.

The remarkable properties of lavender were rediscovered in 1928 by the French chemist René Gattefossé, who, on plunging his badly burned hand into a vat of lavender, was amazed by the oil's incredible healing powers. The French surgeon, Jean Valnet, also used lavender to treat burns and injuries during World War II.

The chemistry

Lavender has a complex chemical structure. The balance of natural chemicals in the oil can vary, depending on where the lavender is grown, soil and weather conditions. Its active ingredients are esters of butyric acid and valerianic acid, ether of linalyl and geranyl, geraniol, linalol, cineol, d-borneol, limonene, l-pinene, caryophyllene and coumarin. This means lavender is analgesic, bactericidal, decongestant, sedative and an insect repellent.

General use

Lavender neutralizes, harmonizes and balances. It soothes the mind, promotes balance for nervous exhaustion and is useful for general debility. It is sedating, antidepressant and will help with insomnia and headaches. Both relaxing and stimulating, it calms refreshes, invigorates and lifts the spirits. When you are not sure what you need, but know you need a lovely bath with *something*, add six to eight drops of lavender to a full bath.

As a tonic

Lavender is a tonic and seems to have a sedative action on the heart. This makes it a valuable oil both for palpitations and high blood pressure – although you should check with your doctor first. It helps the body deal with tension, tiredness, depression and, while doing so, stimulates the immune system and helps protect the body against infections. Again try a bath with six to eight drops of lavender oil.

Headaches

A drop of neat lavender massaged into each temple will relieve many kinds of headaches. Or you could try a drop on the base of the skull, a cold compress on the forehead or on the back of the neck.

To promote sleep

Add five or six drops to a full bath and soak for at least ten minutes. Then put a couple of drops on the backs of your hands or on your pillow and breathe the aroma in deeply as you go to sleep. This will greatly enhance the 'counting sheep' technique. I find lavender promotes deep, satisfying sleep.

For the muscles

With muscular pain, rheumatism, arthritis or sciatica lavender can be a real breakthrough. Check first with your doctor or osteopath that your problem is muscular and not structural, that is, not connected with your bones. Then try six to eight drops of lavender

Lavender's ability to help reduce inflammation and pain, along with its cooling action, is invaluable in all types of muscular, arthritic and joint pains.

in your bath or neat on the actual trouble spot. Lavender seems to act in several ways here. It reduces pain and has a calming effect on the central nervous system. Lavender's ability to help reduce inflammation and pain, along with its cooling action, is invaluable in all types of muscular, arthritic and joint pains.

On the skin

Lavender and tea tree are the only essential oils which may be applied directly to the skin without any dilution. Lavender promotes cellular regeneration, helps in the healing of wounds and prevents scarring. I always use it in my face oils. It is great for soothing sunburn, blisters, acne, boils, insect bites and minor burns. Use neat on the affected area or add five drops of lavender to two teaspoons of pure vegetable oil.

Lavender will enhance the actions of other essential oils and is safe to use with babies and children and during pregnancy, although I always recommend using a little less than your usual dose for babies.

TEA TREE

The original tea tree was the New Zealand plant known as manuka (*Leptospermum scoparium*). It was named tea tree by Captain Cook as the native people, the Maori, used the plant in their natural medicine and made tea from the leaves and bark. Cook wrote, 'It has an agreeable but bitter taste and flavour when the leaves are recent, but loses some of both when they are dried'.

There are over 300 different types of shrubs and trees commonly referred to as 'ti' trees throughout Australia and New Zealand. These trees usually fall into two genera: *Leptospermum* and *Melaleuca*, both of which are part of the *Myrtaceae* family, along with cajeput, myrtle, clove, eucalyptus and niaouli. The variety that is considered to have the most therapeutic properties is *Melaleuca alternifolia* which comes from the plantations of New South Wales, Australia. The oil is extracted using steam distillation.

Help your body generally to ward off any bacterial, fungal or viral infection

For me, tea tree oil is the second most essential, essential oil. It is always in my travelling kit. It is great for 'dirty'cuts or spots. It is the best thing to add to water to gargle with when you have a sore throat and great to inhale when you have an oncoming cold or sinus discomfort caused by air-conditioning. It will help your body generally to ward off any bacterial, fungal or viral infection. It is both anti-septic and anti-fungal.

Background history

Originally used by Maoris in New Zealand and Aborigines in Australia, the leaves of the tree were crushed and applied to cuts, skin infections and wounds, which would then be covered with a mud pack. When Europeans arrived, they adopted the local medicine, as their own was too difficult to obtain. Tea tree oil enjoyed a long spell of usage and acceptance up until the middle of this century, when commercially produced drugs became more widely available. Tea tree was soon regarded as a second-rate medicine. In the 1930s tea tree was studied and written about in several medical journals, including the British and American Medical Journals in 1933. During World War II, the production of tea tree oil was considered an essential industry and its workers were not forced to enlist. At the end of the war the oil was almost impossible to get. Then came the era of penicillin, and it was not until the 1960s and '70s, when natural products became popular again, that tea tree oil started its comeback. Now, as the demand for tea tree oil grows, many plantations are developing in New South Wales, Australia. One of the great advantages of the tea tree is that it is only the leaves that are harvested, which quickly regrow.

Chemistry of the oil

Tea tree contains at least forty-eight organic compounds. Its active ingredients include terpineol, cineol, terpinene, sesquiterpinenes, sesquiterpinene alcohols, cymones and pinene. Sword and Hunter's 1978 detailed analysis of tea tree oil revealed it to contain viridiflorene, B terpineol, L-terpineol and allyhexanoate. These are rarely, if ever, found in nature – in fact this was the first time an organic source of viridiflorene had been found – and it is the combination of these four substances that give tea tree oil its amazing healing properties.

Tea tree is a most amazing antiseptic. It has been shown to have antiseptic qualities thirteen times stronger than carbolic acid, yet none of the skin irritation side-effects and it is nontoxic. It seems tea tree oil has a powerful germicidal action, yet causes none of the tissue damage that one would expect from so strong an oil. The two fascinating aspects of tea tree which set it apart from the other members of its *Myrtaceae* family are:

- it is a powerful stimulant of the immune system. When the body is fighting infection tea tree will support and increase the body's ability to respond.
- tea tree will fight bacteria, viruses and fungi.

General uses

Tea tree has a wide range of antiseptic uses. It is excellent for sinus problems and catarrh. Inhaling a couple of drops from a tissue or vaporizing two drops of lemon with two drops of tea tree in a burner when colds are in the air is really effective.

It is also a marvellous treatment for athlete's foot, ringworm, and, under the guidance of your aromatherapist, may also be extremely helpful in treating candida and thrush. Such a wide range of conditions may benefit from the use of tea tree oil, (including boils, abcesses, cystitis, dermatitis and varicose ulcers) that I will only outline the most straightforward in this book. For more serious ailments, it is best to get a good diagnosis from your doctor first, before consulting your aromatherapist for the correct usage.

Tea Tree Tonic

With tea tree's ability to stimulate the immune system, this is a good oil to use if you repeatedly go down with minor infections – although you should always consult your GP as well – or are slow to recover from any illness. By taking a bath containing tea tree you will help to support the immune system. Fill your bath, then add about six drops of tea tree oil and soak for at least ten minutes.

Colds and Flu

At the first sign of a cold or the achy joints of flu, start taking tea tree baths. Run your bath and add up to six drops of tea tree oil. Soak for ten minutes which may bring on profuse

> At the first sign of a cold or the achy joints of flu start taking tea tree baths.

sweating. This is the body ridding itself of the infection and is a natural and healthy response to an infection or virus. This may even be enough to stop the cold or flu catching hold but, if not, they will be far less severe as the tea tree will be stimulating the body to fight them.

Insect Bites

A natural insect repellent, tea tree may be dabbed neat onto the skin before or after being bitten. This will help to dissipate the itching and prevent infection that sometimes occurs with bites. Tea tree will also provide fast relief from wasp or bee stings. Add two drops to one teaspoon of pure vegetable oil and rub on your skin as a prevention treatment, or simply add a few drops to your body lotion and mix well.

Warts and verrucae

Try a single drop of tea tree oil on the centre of a wart or veruca every day and cover with a plaster or melolin square. This treatment needs persistence. Keep up this daily routine for several weeks and continue for two weeks after you think the wart has completely gone.

Cold Sores

Neat tea tree oil on cold sores is very effective. Start applying one neat drop when you first get the burning sensation or tightness that comes before the blister appears. Try to do this two to three times a day until the skin feels 'normal' again. Tea tree may be used in the same way for the blisters of shingles and chicken pox. They are all infections of the same virus.

Dental Care

Tea tree is great for freshening the breath and taking extra care of your gums. Gargle and rinse your mouth daily with two drops of tea tree and one drop of lemon in half a glass of water. You can use the tea tree oil on its own but I like the added freshness and cleansing action of the lemon. You can dab neat tea tree oil on sore gums as well – at least until you can get to see your dentist. A daily routine of this gargling and rinsing will really help maintain a clean mouth, teeth and healthy gums.

Spots

Tea tree is wonderful for getting rid of spots and acne (for severe acne, see your aromatherapist for a monitored programme). You can dab a neat drop of oil on the spot itself, three to four times a day – the results will amaze you! It is also good in soap – try to find one that contains two per cent tea tree oil if you can. Or alternatively mix youself a face wash: add five drops to a handbasin filled a third of the way with water and rinse your face. You could also try applying one teaspoon of pure vegetable oil mixed with three drops of tea tree to clean skin. See the section on skin for other recipes.

Tea tree oil, with its wide ranging antiseptic properties, is an asset to any household. Start to use it, get to know it – its abilities are nothing short of miraculous!

INTUITION

This is a flabby muscle for most of us. Just like a muscle, it can be toned and developed with regular use. Use essential oils to give yourself an 'intuition workout'.

Each time you choose a new essential oil, smell several that you think you might like or have similar qualities as others you know. Then take the one you are most attracted to by smell. Get to know this oil by its name, colour and texture. See if you can find out what the plant looks like – is it spiky, heavy, delicate or earthy? What does it remind you of and where does it take you?

How do all these aspects contribute to the 'feel' of the oil? As you use it, or even as you smell it, draw on all your senses to 'sense' the oil. Then begin to read about its qualities. Are they similar to what you yourself have 'sensed'? If you are choosing a bath blend, choose with an open mind the oils you are attracted to at that moment. Then go and look up their therapeutic qualities. After a while you will develop a knowledge base. That, combined with your intuition, will enable you to really utilize oils. Sometimes a certain oil may be just right, even though it may not be the logical choice. Remember, too, that oils are seasonal and can come from different countries. Once your intuition gets going, you'll realize how this can alter the effect oils can have on you.

It took me a long time to regularly mix beautiful baths for myself. Now I'm making up for lost time! I close my eyes on the train after a hard day's work and listen to my body. It gives me my bath recipe. And, like food, I look forward to it with delicious expectation. I know there are others of you – I am not alone here!

PART TWO

Applications
for Everyday

STRESS RELIEVERS

We all suffer from stress at times and have to find ways of dealing with it effectively. One of the positive aspects of writing this book, while trying to run a small and growing business, work with oils and find time to relax is that you really *have* to practise what you preach!

The first thing you need to do is admit you are stressed. Then ask yourself: are you able to deal with the source of it, or do you need to find help? Many different aspects of your working life can cause stress – even incorrect lighting can contribute to it. Can you work out a way to avoid it? Can anything in your working or home life be simplified?

To combat the symptoms of stress, I would highly recommend going for regular aromatherapy massage throughout the stressful period. The massage itself works wonders and you will get specific help through the use of the oils chosen for you. You can then supplement this treatment with the DIY approach.

THE DIY APPROACH

Any oil that you like the smell of and is relaxing is good for you in times of stress. Bathe in it, wear it, vaporize it in a burner.

Relaxing and mentally/emotionally uplifting oils such as bergamot, jasmine,

Black pepper, thyme and peppermint should only be used in time of exhaustion and stress

clary sage, lavender, marjoram, neroli, chamomile, rose or vetiver can be really useful in the treatment of stress. Geranium and rosemary are also most helpful – both strengthen the adrenal glands, which work overtime during stressful periods. However, geranium and rosemary should only be used on a short-term basis. NEVER USE THESE OILS LONG TERM.

Other oils that help, such as black pepper, thyme and peppermint, should only be used in time of exhaustion and stress.

Try the following blends:

either		*or*	
geranium	5 drops	vetiver	2 drops
chamomile	5 drops	lemon	5 drops
lavender	5 drops	chamomile	5 drops

Mix either of these blends in 30ml of base oil. Use in your bath or take it to work and dab a little on the backs of your hands or on your pulse points to inhale and benefit from as the day goes by.

You can substitute any of the oils mentioned above but remember they are not to be used long term. After a week to ten days have a break. You may like to try one of these blends in your bath twice a week or just on your major stress days.

During the past few months, which have been tough on my time and energy, these oils have been a real godsend. Changing my thinking pattern was more of a challenge! I really had to allow my perception of events to change. Many ways of coping will come to you if you are able to let go in your 'rest' times. Try and laugh at the situation if possible. Then go back and tackle it again. I am sure we are not meant to live in a constant state of 'doing' but sometimes it is hard to break the habit. Have a go – get creative!

HELPFUL TIPS FOR COPING

Start with this as a guide and invent your own curious ways!

Vitamin supplements Emotional, mental and physical stress will deplete the body of key nutrients and make absorption of these more difficult. It is a good idea to take a supplement at these times. Try extra vitamin C and extra vitamin B complex, or a herbal tonic.

Exercise This can help enormously. Do something regularly that you enjoy, even if you are tired. Don't push it if you are tired – just let go into it and concentrate on your breathing. Take a brisk walk to refocus – walk for twenty minutes in the morning to the station or bus stop, or get off the train or bus a stop earlier and walk the rest of the way to work. Inhale deeply while you do.

Breathing Become more conscious of your breathing. Try the following breathing exercise: inhale for four counts, hold your breath for four counts, then exhale for four counts and hold your breath out for four counts (when I walk I count my steps – breathe in for four steps, hold for four steps, breathe out for four, hold out for four). You can imagine the breath coming up from the ground, up one side of your body and down the other and back into the ground again. The important thing is to have a rhythm and repeat it. The counting can help as it gives the brain something to do – which stops you worrying!

Concentrating When things get really tough I try to concentrate on each thing I'm doing. Write down a list of what you have to do. Then just concentrate on each thing as you do it – don't worry about the other things. When you've finished the first job, concentrate on the second. I still end up doing several things at once, but my mistake rate, confusion rate and heart rate seem to remain lower when I do this. It's very effective.

Baths Even when I'm exhausted a bath is always worth the effort. Ten minutes in the bath and I'm able to get a good night's sleep or re-energize myself so I can face the world again. Try the stress recipes or even a relaxing blend of oils.

We all have a certain amount of day-to-day stress. But there are times when life is more stressful than normal and, until you can deal with the source of it, looking after your body and finding ways to relax is imperative. I have found that using the oils and the suggestions above have helped me enormously and they will you too.

CONCENTRATION AND STUDYING

Essential oils can be a great tool when intense concentration is called for. Use these oils only when you need them. Avoid using them all the time.

LEMON

This fruit is cultivated for the extraction of essential oil throughout the Mediterranean and in California. The oil is expressed (pressed out) from the outer rind of the fruit. The active ingredients include pinene, camphene, linalol, actetates of linalol and geranyl, limonene, phelladrene, citral and citronellal.

Lemon has a number of important properties:

- it stimulates the white corpuscles to defend the body against infection
- it will assist in reducing high body temperature during flu and colds
- it has a haemostatic action – that is, it helps to stop bleeding
- it is powerful in killing bacteria
- it has a tonic effect on the circulatory system

Studies in Japan have shown that computer users make fifty-three per cent fewer errors when their workspace is fragranced with lemon.

When studying, lemon helps to clear the air and the brain. Studies in Japan have shown that computer users make fifty-three per cent fewer errors when their workspace is fragranced with lemon. This kind of fragrancing is fairly standard in many Japanese companies now.

PEPPERMINT

This essential oil is also native to Europe and is grown largely in America now. The active constituents of peppermint are menthol, phelladrene, limonene, menthene and mentone.

Peppermint is best known for its effectiveness in dealing with digestive upsets. It has been known for these properties for thousands of years. Peppermint is helpful at the onset of a cold or flu: it can induce sweating which helps the body deal with fever in a natural way and is also a good decongestant. Peppermint stimulates the brain and aids clear thinking. When used in the bath do not use more than three drops as this oil can irritate the skin. It should not be used over a long period. It promotes wakefulness and can upset your normal sleep patterns.

BASIL

This herb has been valued for centuries for cooking and medicinal use, from chest infections to digestive problems. Widely used for headaches and migraines, basil was made into powder and taken as snuff to clear the head in the sixteenth century. Along with peppermint, basil is a 'cephalic' oil which stimulates the brain, clears the head and is good for mental fatigue. Only use two to three drops in the bath as basil too can irritate the skin. It can be a very effective oil but is best used sparingly and rarely. Many people swear by it, so use your intuition. Mine says: every now and then with this oil.

Here are some practical recipes to try.

When you're working late into the night on a project or cramming into the wee hours, blend together:

| lemon | 2 drops |
| peppermint | 2 drops |

Vaporize in an oil burner or put the drops on a tissue and inhale. For important interviews, exams and tough meetings, try:

either		*or*	
lavender	3 drops	petitgrain	3 drops
bergamot	2 drops	grapefruit	3 drops

in your bath before you head off in the morning. If you shower, then add the drops to your flannel and give yourself a body rub in or after your shower. You could also try putting a couple of drops on a tissue to inhale which you could take with you.

To get to sleep the night before an interview, exam or meeting, try adding:

either		*or*	
sandalwood	4 drops	lavender	4 drops
lemon	3 drops	bergamot	3 drops

to your bath. Remember to run the bath first and have at least a ten-minute soak. If you prefer vaporizing oils, these can be used in a burner to help you wind down before going to sleep.

When a project just has to be done *now* and you need to muster all your focus, clarity and concentration, try burning some of these combinations in your workspace:

either		*or*	
neroli	3 drops	grapefruit	4 drops
bergamot	3 drops	geranium	2 drops

These will help you to focus and urge the 'doer' parts of your brain into action.

Other oils which may be substituted in these blends as you get to know them are: rosemary, coriander and palma rosa.

Remember that these oils are powerful. But they are surely better for you than some of the chemical substances we use to keep ourselves awake and alert. Use them only when you need them most, not all the time. They can really help your body to summon and direct its own abilities.

THE WORK ENVIRONMENT

We spend so much time at work, we need to create as healthy a space as we can. One of the most important things lacking in most offices is a good water source. Headaches and concentration difficulties can be avoided if your body is well hydrated. If your office doesn't have one, ask if a fountain or other water source can be installed. Make sure you drink at least a litre of water a day. You'll soon get used to it and stop running to the toilet all the time. And you'll feel so much better.

YOUR OWN DESK SPACE

You may not be able to convince the entire office to use aromatherapy in their environment. However, as you use it in your own smaller space you may find a few initially uninterested people become interested. People will be secretly fascinated by it all, especially as they observe it working for you. On your desk you may like to keep a range of blended oils in small bottles containing the help you need specifically for work. You could keep a bottle of Hangover Blend, for example, for those odd times when you or a colleague need extra help. A small mix of concentrated oil is a good idea too. Blended oils can always be used on the back of your hand and inhaled discreetly, or dropped onto a tissue. Cotton wool on the radiator can gently permeate your office space with whatever you happen to need at the time. A blend for stress would probably come in handy too! All these blends are in the various sections of the book, so go ahead and look them up. Here are a few other ideas for the conversion of your office space.

HEADACHES

As I mentioned above, it is very important to keep yourself well hydrated. Sometimes we get so carried away with work that we forget to drink. The headache this causes is very distinctive and is totally remedied by drinking water. Another real cause of headaches is office lighting. Many older offices have terrible lighting, especially those with fluorescent tubes. Sometimes it is possible to alter the lighting – do whatever you can to soften your general lighting but make sure you have your work itself well lit, for example with a good desk lamp. Headaches from fluorescent and bright lighting can be soothed by rosemary or a rosemary/lavender blend. Try inhaling a couple of drops of rosemary from a tissue or adding it to your diffuser. If you find you regularly suffer from headaches at a certain time of the day, say mid-afternoon, put some rosemary/lavender drops in your diffuser and set it going after lunch. You could well find that your usual headache does not materialize.

COLDS AND FLU

Workplaces are notorious for spreading airborne infections like colds and flu. Poor ventilation is often one of the reasons why. If you have air-conditioning there seems to be no escape from the viruses that spread through buildings. Oils that help combat bacteria and viruses are lavender, tea tree, eucalyptus and lemon. If you can, suggest to your office manager or health and safety representative that the company diffuse oils through the air-conditioning system in the colds and flu season. Some open-minded companies are already doing this sort of thing with success. However, if this is not possible, at least make an impact on your own small workspace. When the cold season is beginning, add to your diffuser, or your tissue, tea tree and lemon. The tea tree will stimulate your immune system and the lemon is beautifully cleansing and has the added bonus of clearing your head, thereby helping your concentration. It is a good companion to tea tree oil, which can smell rather medicinal on its own. At the merest hint of a sniffle or cough, increase your intake of vitamin C, drink lots of water and inhale tea tree oil. I am constantly amazed how the most violent of colds and flu can then just pass me by. Alternatively, lavender and eucalyptus are interchangeable with tea tree and lemon. A couple of drops of lavender and tea tree will work well on a tissue to inhale, as will lavender and eucalyptus. Be guided by your personal preference and intuition.

> *At the merest hint of a sniffle or cough, increase your intake of vitamin C, drink lots of water and inhale tea tree oil.*

CONCENTRATION

If your mind is wandering and you need that extra surge of energy from somewhere, peppermint, lemon, grapefruit and basil oils will help. A drop of one of these oils, or a combination of two, will really make the difference. The 'cotton wool on the radiator' method is a handy way to get the oil into the air around you. Or drops on a tissue to inhale at work is just as effective. Blending the oils with a base oil which you can then take with you to work is a good idea. Rub this blend into the backs of your hands and inhale it throughout the day.

GENERAL COMPLAINTS

Working in a large building or air-conditioned space can cause other problems that, though minor, are continually annoying.

- **Dry, itchy eyes.** These are commonly reported. Try lavender and tea tree in your diffusing mechanism or inhale drops on a tissue.
- **Dry throat.** Try tea tree oil and lemon, using the methods above. Or you could gargle morning and evening with two drops of tea tree oil and one drop of lemon in half a glass of water.
- **General malaise.** When you're just not feeling good try lavender and grapefruit in your workspace, using the methods above, and also in your morning bath or shower.

Although I still prefer the traditional oil burner with the natural candle, some very interesting and simple methods of diffusing oils without candles are now available. Both electrically run and battery-run diffusers – which have a fan mechanism – both work well and are practical for the workplace. I'm sure we will see some innovative designs for these diffusers over the next few years.

MAJOR UNWIND

Every week I dream of being able to do this. I used to think there was something very self-indulgent about spending a few hours just looking after my body and really relaxing. Now I see it as essential maintenance and would love to be able to do this weekly. The Romans knew a thing or two when they made bathing a social event. Can you imagine meeting up with friends and, instead of going to a bar, going for a bath? In New Zealand we are very lucky to have beautiful natural springs, so that's exactly what we do. A Friday night at the hot pools is a great way to end the week and start the weekend and aromatherapy is included these days. So what does a Kiwi do outside her natural habitat? Here are some of the things that work for me.

SELECTING YOUR OILS

If you are setting time aside for yourself it is a good exercise to let your intuition out for an airing. Line up your oils so you can't see the labels, sit for a moment or two, take in all the bottles and feel what you need to burn in your space today. Ask yourself the question, 'What do I need most right now?' – out loud if you can. When are you ready, choose two oils. If you don't know much about the ones you've chosen, go and look them up and see if these are the ones you need. It always surprises me how accurate this can be if you allow it. If you've chosen oils that don't seem at all right, think again. They may be the right oils without you realizing it. Or try picking the oils again and let go as much as you can. You'll get better at this with practice – I never trusted myself to begin with and it took a while for me to let go of being 'right'. Just try it and you'll get there.

If the idea of letting your intuition do the choosing doesn't appeal, and you just want something relaxing, one of these combinations may appeal to you:

either		*or*
lavender	2 drops	geranium 2 drops
bergamot	1 drop	orange 2 drops
or		
lavender	2 drops	
grapefruit	2 drops	

Whichever oils you have chosen, and however you have chosen them, start setting the atmosphere by burning them.

While the oils are burning, I like to take care of my feet. For recipes to try here see the 'Treat the Feet' section on pages 79 to 82. First of all, I soak my feet, then clean and file the nails. Finally I give my feet a scrub to get rid of any dry skin. I then move onto my hair and treat it to a hair tonic (see the Beauty section, pages 111–12). I leave this tonic on while I'm in the bath. Just before I get into the bath I brush my body with a natural bristle brush – this feels great and is wonderful for the circulation and condition of the skin.

Finish with a deeply unwinding bath. Let your intuition out once again to choose your oils, or you might like to try one of the blends above – though do feel free to invent your own. For this section I'd like to highlight vetiver. This is a deeply relaxing and somewhat underrated essential oil.

VETIVER

This oil is extracted from a scented grass related to citronella and lemongrass, although you would never think so to smell it. It is native to India and Sri Lanka but can be found cultivated in other parts of the world now, too. The extraction of this oil requires a lot of labour, as the roots of the grass have to be dug up and washed before the long distillation process can begin. The major chemical components of this oil are vetiverol, vetiverone, vitivene and cadinene. The aroma is very earthy and smoky. There is little resemblance to lemongrass until the oil is quite dilute.

Vetiver oil is often used in modern perfumery as a fixative and bass note. The roots have for centuries been used in India for their perfume. The Indian name for vetiver means 'oil of tranquillity' and this perfectly encapsulates the feeling of the oil. Vetiver is so deeply relaxing, destressing, it just dissolves anxiety and is great for serious unwinding. I am still surprised by the impact of this oil on me, even knowing how it works. After just one vertiver bath you will be ready to take on another week of life! Vetiver is an immuno-stimulant and this makes it a good choice for stressful times, as stress can really undermine the immune system.

Vetiver is not only used in perfumery, it is also added to skincare products for oily or problem skins. With its earthy aroma, it is great in skincare blends for men and blends beautifully with sandalwood, cedarwood and lavender.

UNWINDING BLENDS

My all-time favourite for unwinding is:

vetiver	2 drops
chamomile	2 drops
lemon	1 drop

Adding this blend to a full bath and soaking for ten minutes always restores me to my relaxed self and will guarantee an excellent night's sleep.

Another excellent blend is:

lavender	3 drops
benzoin	2 drops
bergamot	1 drop

Benzoin is warming, soothing and lovely when blended with the relaxing qualities of lavender and uplifting bergamot. However, one word of warning: benzoin shouldn't be used in a plastic bath as it may damage the surface.

I also recommend:

lavender	2 drops
chamomile	2 drops
geranium	2 drops

This is particularly destressing, will help soothe any anxiety and restore your balance.

Another different 'flavour' to try for unwinding is:

sandalwood	3 drops
chamomile	1 drop
clary sage	1 drop

This blend is wonderfully relaxing, lovely for your skin and excellent if you are a worrier.

I find it very soothing to have lighted candles around my bath. Soft music or no music also tends to be more conducive to relaxation. Most of these blends are great skin oils, too. Try massaging your body while you're in the bath and you will benefit more from them. Or you could mix your bath blend with 10ml of carrier oil and give yourself a massage before you have a soak. There are so many different permutations for you to try – experiment and do what you find works best for you.

DETOXING

I think too much is made of the detoxification process today. Detoxification is only important as part of the whole process of maintaining a healthy system. The key is balance. Let's look at some of the factors critical in maintaining this balance:

WATER

Most people do not drink enough pure water. This does not include water in your tea or coffee – what I mean is pure, unadulterated mineral water. Two litres is the ideal amount for most bodies each day no matter what else you have in your diet. At first, most people find that two litres is too much, so start by increasing your intake. I guarantee you will begin to feel better in yourself after about three consecutive days of drinking more. Most of the year I personally find that one and a half litres of water is just the right amount for me. In the summer I can drink two litres, sometimes more. Your body has to adjust to the higher water intake, though, if you are not used to it. So give it a bit of time and gently the increase the amount.

NUTRITION

If you added two litres of water and as much fresh fruit and vegetables as you can eat to your daily diet, you would lose weight.
The body knows it is receiving regular 'good' food when it constantly burns everything it can. Eating regularly helps establish
this pattern. If you starve your body, it shuts down the energy-
generating systems and stores everything it can. To lose weight
in a healthy way, you need to let your body know it will receive
regular food so it can continue to burn energy. Feed it regularly,
with 'real' food, not 'junk' food full of additives with no food
value. Try to eat as much raw fruit and raw vegetables as you
can. Try steaming the vegetables you do cook – they seem to
taste much better than boiled, they cook quickly and there are
fewer pots to wash up! Fresh juices are a good supplement to
your diet too. Try carrot, beetroot, spinach and cucumber juices
– they all contain important vitamins and minerals, along with
fibre that we require in our diets. All raw fibre, present in raw
food, travels through the colon or bowel faster than cooked
fibre. It tends to make you feel lighter. The fibre in raw foods
also tends to have a clearing, cleansing action on the wall of the
bowel. This keeps the bowel free of build-ups of toxic material
from the 'bad' foods we take in.

EXERCISE

Even if the only exercise you take is a brisk walk every day it is
still terribly important. If you can, get fresh air with your exercise. Whatever you do, do *something* and try your best to do it
regularly. If you really enjoy swimming or cycling, try to incorpo-
rate it into your life in a natural way so you'll be more inclined
to keep it up. Regular exercise is essential to a healthy system.

WORK

The role of work in our lives has come under the spotlight late-
ly with many people choosing less pressurized jobs with lower
salaries in favour of a better quality of life. We are all different

and require various challenges, respites and time out at different times of our lives. My only advice is to try to be sensitive to what *you* need. It is so tempting to do what we believe is required of us or what our education has set us up for. Asking the question, 'What do I actually want to work at and how can this give me the life I would like?' and being brave enough to follow the answer is the path to balance and fulfilment. It may not feel like it at first, but further down the road you will start to reap the benefits.

PLAY

Time out, leisure, socializing – we all need this in some form or other. It is an important a part of life as the other aspects. Does play form an equal part of *your* life?

I think these are the main areas of life that require balancing. The amount of attention we can devote to each will change constantly and none of us will feel we have them in balance for more than a few days at a time. Everything fluctuates.

> *When our system does lose its balance we may have to take action to restore it.*

When our system does lose its balance we may have to take action to restore it. It may only be necessary to redress our thinking patterns – which is more often than not the case – and reassess our priorities. Or we may need to pay attention to our diet for a while, or consciously drink more water, or get more sleep or rest until we're back on track.

If, however, some imbalances have been with us for a long period of time, they may now have consequences. Cellulite is a common and much talked about one. But you don't have to live with it. Here's how you can do something about it.

CELLULITE ATTACK

Cellulite results from toxicity in the body of some sort. Whether this is an imbalance in the endocrine system (glands and hormones), caused primarily by an allergy, the result of poor lymph drainage and circulation problems, or the outcome of a long period of imbalance within our bodies, these unsightly, fatty deposits can become the bane of our lives. Redressing this balance may take some determined work over a period of time, but you will end up altogether healthier for it. Use the following as a guide to your cellulite-attacking strategy.

Diet. Take a good look at your diet. Read the section on nutrition above and take on board as many suggestions as you can. Allow yourself to introduce the changes to your diet gradually – you don't have to adopt everything at once. I would also cut out dairy products as far as possible. Make sure you eat plenty of rice and pulses. To your water or cups of tea – try a few herbal ones to wean yourself off tea and coffee – add one drop of lemon essential oil to one cup daily and one cup of rosemary oil to one cup daily. Make sure you do not take vitamin and mineral supplements derived from yeast and try to take 1000mg of vitamin C per day. Vitamin B complex and zinc are also recommended.

Skin Brushing. Find yourself a natural bristle brush and get into the habit of brushing your skin daily before your shower or bath. Always brush towards the heart. Skin brushing will stimulate your circulation and help with lymph drainage. It also makes your skin really soft and silky. It feels really wonderful, too.

Exercise. Make yourself exercise in some form daily. Walking is great. Try to take lots of deep breaths. If there are lots of trees and water on your daily walk so much the better – it will do your soul good too.

Massage. If you can, massage all of you. If you are running short on time, massage only the areas of cellulite and lymph glands – under your arms, around your neck and in your groin area – with one of the blends below. These glands should be massaged in tiny circles. Here are two massage blends that I recommend for cellulite:

To 50ml of carrier oil add:

either		*or*	
fennel	8 drops	fennel	9 drops
juniper	6 drops	grapefruit	10 drops
rosemary	8 drops	lemon	9 drops
lemon	6 drops		

Baths. Use the blends of your choice in the bath and try these special salt baths twice a week for six weeks, then once a week: throw one cupful of Epsom salts into your bath, run the water, and when your bath is full, add:

either		*or*	
rosemary	2 drops	lemon	2 drops
grapefruit	3 drops	juniper	2 drops
fennel	2 drops	rosemary	2 drops

SLEEPING WELL

In my work, selling essential oils and blends, I have noticed a growing awareness of the uses of lavender, especially its ability to promote sleep. More and more people are discovering natural alternatives to sleeping tablets. I hope they will also begin to discover some of the other good side-effects this oil has on your general health.

As well as lavender, other oils effective at promoting sleep are chamomile and marjoram. I have covered lavender and chamomile elsewhere in this book, so let's take a brief look here at marjoram.

MARJORAM

Marjoram is native to Europe and Central Asia. Its name comes from the Latin word 'major', because in ancient times this plant

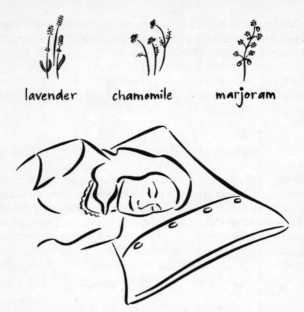

lavender   chamomile   marjoram

was thought to extend the lifespan. It was a popular plant in England, and most English houses grew it in their herb gardens. Culpeper wrote in his herbal that marjoram was so well known as an inhabitant of every garden that a description of the herb was unnecessary. The essential oil, which is distilled from the entire plant, has a warm, camphorous and rather sweet aroma. The active constituents of marjoram include borneol, sabinene, camphor, pinene and origanol.

Marjoram is beautifully warming and comforting for the mind and body. It is analgesic and sedative. It has been used for centuries in cooking as it has a tonic effect on the digestive tract, aids digestion and relieves constipation. It seems to strengthen the wave-like action within the bowel which moves food along the tract as it is digested.

In ancient times this plant was thought to extend the lifespan

Marjoram can be helpful with insomnia. Bended with lavender in a bath or rub before going to sleep it can work wonders. Massaged over the chest and around the throat, marjoram can be a valuable oil to use for many breathing or chest-related problems, even in common coughs and colds. The sedative properties of marjoram can be rather powerful so this is one of those oils to use under guidance from your aromatherapist until you are very familiar with its effects. It is still one of the oils to use over a short period of time only.

One of the effects of marjoram, and one of the reasons it is so warming, is that it dilates the small blood vessels just under the skin, which makes the skin feel warm to the touch. This increase in circulation in a particular area makes marjoram a valuable oil for tired, tight, overworked muscles and helps to clear the area of toxins and debris left in the muscle after heavy exertion, bringing nutrients to the area via the blood stream. All muscular aches and pains benefit from this oil, and its anti-spasmodic action also helps with muscle spasm. For these same reasons marjoram is good to include in a blend for arthritis and rheumatism.

Another interesting aspect of this oil is its anti-aphrodisiac properties. The effect the oil has on libido has been utilized by religious institutions for many centuries. There may well be times when it is handy to have a bottle in your handbag or pocket!

ENHANCING SLEEP

If you sometimes need just a little help to get you off to sleep, lavender is the oil for you. A couple of drops on your pillow, on the back of your hand or on a tissue, just to breathe in as you lie there, will do the trick and send you off to sleep. Using lavender in this way promotes deeper sleep. You will wake up feeling truly rested.

You could try a drop of lavender and chamomile together in the same way. But remember, you always need to blend chamomile first by adding it to a carrier oil as it cannot be used directly on the skin. Try one teaspoon of base oil with two drops lavender and one of chamomile.

A friend of mine, Jim, who travels a lot has found the blend below – what I call my 'Dreamtime' blend – invaluable in helping him sleep while he travels.

In 50ml carrier oil add:

lavender	16 drops
chamomile	9 drops

Take a little bottle of this mix travelling with you. When you are settled and ready for your journey, put a little on your face. This way you inhale it easily (the lazy way!). Then, with the little left on your hands rub your palms together briskly, inhale from your hands deeply and just close your eyes. Using this technique, Jim sleeps through many a take-off when flying and knows nothing more until rudely awakened upon landing! A bonus of using these two oils in this way is that both lavender and chamomile are lovely for the skin. This gives you even more reason to try them.

THE WORKS

If you are really troubled by lack of sleep, try and find the cause. If it is obvious and you are able do something to change or alter your life, then go ahead. If you can't change things, then try some of these ways to keep you going until you are able to alter your lifestyle.

- Exercise more regularly and breathe deeply as you do. Even walking for twenty minutes will help.
- Try putting neat lavender on the backs of your hands, a little on your chest and on the back of your neck where your neck joins your head. Inhale as you go to sleep.

Run a bath and add either of these blends:

either		*or*	
lavender	3 drops	lavender	3 drops
chamomile	2 drops	marjoram	3 drops

Before you wallow in your bath, set your burner going with two drops of lavender and one drop of chamomile or you may choose from vetiver, benzoin and clary sage if you'd like something different. Get to know what works well for *you*. Have a quiet soak in the bath and light some candles as an alternative to full lighting.

> *Oils in larger doses can be stimulating rather than relaxing, so as far as getting a good night's sleep goes, less is more.*

This will calm the whole system down. But don't think that using more of oils – especially lavender, chamomile and marjorum – will help you to sleep better. Oils in larger doses can be stimulating rather than relaxing, so as far as getting a good night's sleep goes, less is more.

LITTLE PEOPLE

Even little people – those under twelve years – can suffer from sleeplessness. If it continues for some time, ensure that you consult a profressional. But a short period of sleeplessness can be normal in healthy children. It may be the result of nightmares, very busy days and worrying about school things. Having a wind-down time before bed seems to be the best solution. Switch the television off and run a warm bath with some oils – both comforting and relaxing. Cuddles and stories can help too – and that's the same for big people!

When using oils in the bath, remember that children's bodies are very sensitive so the oils must be used in a very dilute form.

For children up to five years old choose a maximum of three drops from either lavender, chamomile or mandarin. Always run the bath first before adding the oils. You may use less oil – just two drops of lavender rather than three – but make sure you do not exceed a total of three drops.

For children of about five to twelve years, choose a maximum of five drops from one of the following: lavender, chamomile, mandarin, geranium and clary sage. Always use geranium and clary sage with another of the oils.

I find children love the smells of the oils and really enjoy having them in their baths. It makes them feel special – and you too will enjoy the results!

BUG BUSTERS

Essential oils appear to work miracles in fighting off and treating the symptoms of colds and flu. I rely on tea tree, lavender and eucalyptus, individually or together, with thyme, marjoram, naiouli, lemon, benzoin and rosemary as backups or variations. To remind yourself of the benefits of lavender and tea tree, read pages 15 to 23. In this section, I would like to look at the other 'wonder' oil: eucalyptus.

EUCALYPTUS

This plant has made its name in history as a good decongestant for colds, flu and catarrh. Its anti-viral and bactericidal actions are probably less known but just as powerful. Inhaling eucalyptus is a natural treatment for colds as it soothes the respiratory passages. At the same time it prevents the spread of the cold virus throughout the system.

Inhaling eucalyptus is a natural treatment for colds

There are many varieties of eucalyptus – about 300 in all. The most commonly found essential oil is from the Australian blue-gum variety - *Eucalyptus globulus*. If you can find it, *Eucalyptus radiata* is lovely in aromatherapy as it has a more pleasing aroma and is less inclined to irritate the skin.

The main constituents of *Eucalyptus globulus* are eucalyptol (which makes up eighty per cent), camphene, eudesmol, ethyl alcohol, amyl alcohol, aldehydes, phellandrene, pinene and aromadendrene. *Eucalyptus radiata* is more like the tea tree family (*Melaleucas*) with slightly less eucalyptol (seventy per cent), terpineol and some monoterpenes.

Jean Valnet, the father of aromatherapy as we know it, gave very precise information about eucalyptus and its bactericidal properties. He claimed that: 'a spray containing two per cent eucalyptus will kill seventy per cent of staphylococci in the air'. The potency of this essential oil is far greater than each of its chemical constituents. Eucalyptol, used in many pharmaceutical preparations, is not nearly as effective as the essential oil itself. One of the reasons for this is that the aromadendrenes and phellandrenes have a chemical reaction to the oxygen in the air and produce ozone, and bacteria cannot live in this environment.

Australian aborigines have used eucalyptus leaves on wounds for centuries. It is renowned as a useful treatment in urinary tract infections and helps to relieve pain in rheumatism.

AT FIRST SIGN OF COLDS AND FLU

As soon as you feel cold symptoms coming on, or if everyone around you is coming down with something, start your body support strategy. Using the oils will encourage your own body's natural lines of defence and give them a boost. The strategy uses baths and inhalations.

The body support strategy

Start by getting tea tree oil into your system. Add a couple of drops to a tissue in your pocket, or up your sleeve, and inhale it while you are working. If you are feeling unwell, have a bath containing up to five drops of tea tree oil that night and steam clean your body. If you prefer, you could try three drops of tea tree and three of lavender. The lavender will work with the tea tree and many people will prefer the smell. Sit in your bath and inhale deeply. If you do this before you go to bed the oils will help you into a deep sleep which will also assist your body in healing itself. You'll wake up feeling refreshed and ready for the world again.

Drink lots of pure water and make sure you are taking extra vitamin C (up to 2000mg) over the next few days.

Aching body If you get the shivers and aching limbs run yourself a bath with three drops of lavender and three of marjoram and soak for at least ten minutes. These oils will also help with the headaches you sometimes get at the onset of a cold or flu.

> **Sore Throat** If a sore throat is the first sign of a cold, put two drops of tea tree and one of lemon in half a glass of water. Gargle as often as you can in those first twenty-four hours to combat the bugs!

Coughs Coughing is a reflex action of the respiratory system to try to clear the passages for air to flow freely. This is a natural protective mechanism of our bodies and I don't feel it should be suppressed. However, we can help the body deal with the cause of the cough. Dust, mucus from an infection, catarrh and inflammation can all cause coughs. Good old-fashioned inhalation can be a great boon here. Even if the cough is just irritable, not necessarily part of a cold, this is a good recipe to try. Pour boiling water into a bowl, add two drops each of tea tree, lemon, eucalyptus and benzoin. Cover your head with a towel, close your eyes and inhale with your head about twelve inches from the water. Stay there for as long ten minutes if you can – allowing yourself out from under the towel a couple of times for a break if you need to.

Massage to the throat and chest may also be helpful using these oils: tea tree, eucalyptus, lemon and benzoin. One drop of each in two teaspoons of pure vegetable oil makes a good massage blend.

OTHER WAYS TO USE OILS EFFECTIVELY DURING COLDS AND FLU TIME ARE:

Room spray: add twenty drops of eucalyptus to 50ml of pure water. Spray several times a day throughout the house, particularly in living areas and bedrooms. Great if the whole family may be affected.

Water bowls: before going off to sleep at night put boiling water in a bowl on the floor by the bed. Add two to three drops of each of lavender, tea tree, eucalyptus, marjoram, benzoin and naiouli until you have ten drops in total. It is best to avoid the more stimulating oils at night or it may not be so easy to sleep.

Vaporizing: in an oil burner any time of day or in the evening add up to five drops of any combination of lavender, tea tree, eucalyptus, benzoin, thyme, naiouli, lemon and rosemary.

It is a good idea during the 'cold' season to make up a small bottle of equal parts of the above oils. This mixture can then be vaporized, dropped on boiling water for the old-fashioned inhalation, added to a water bowl at night or to a room spray.

SPOT TREATMENTS

Your skin is a reflection of your general health. If you want to improve your skin, the best place to start is with your diet: include plenty of fresh fruit, raw vegetables and good water. You may need to form 'new habits' in your eating. Refined sugars, artificial additives and saturated fats should be largely avoided, as should tea, coffee, smoking and alcohol. I don't think we should say to ourselves, 'You can *never* eat or drink this or that' – somehow it only makes us want those things more (if I am anything to go by!). Watch your intake of those foods you would benefit from having less of and gradually your diet will improve. If you have a couple of days when you have too much coffee or chocolate, don't berate yourself. Just set your course again and have less of them for the following few days.

Vitamin C makes a real difference to skin. Vitamins E, A and iron do also. Those with problem skin may like to try a zinc supplement as it has proven itself to work well in some cases. These days, so many of the products we eat, especially raw fruit and vegetables, have spent some time out of the ground or off the tree before we actually consume them. By the time their goodness gets into our bodies many of the nutrients are diminished if not lost. For this reason I have taken vitamin C regularly and a herbal tonic (Floradix) twice a year for the past years. Unless we are able to eat our food straight from the garden, I think this is a sensible idea if we are taking care of ourselves. I would recommend taking viatmin C generally, as the vitamin is totally necessary to so many chemical pathways in our bodies. It is an essential ingredient to the healthy functioning of so many minor and major systems within us. I would recommend the addition of vitamins E and A for skin in particular although they do also assist the body in other ways (e.g. can be very helpful in cases of arthritis).

THE OCCASIONAL SPOT
AND PREMENSTRUAL SPOTS

Tea tree oil has the ability to penetrate the surface of the skin. This property makes it excellent for those lumpy spots that can appear prior to our periods. So when you first catch sight of the beginnings of one get out that bottle of tea tree oil, put a neat drop on your clean finger or a cotton bud and apply it directly. Do this three to four times a day if you can. The spot will vanish dramatically.

BLACKHEADS

Treat blackheads with daily use of tea tree oil soap and/or tea tree oil rinses. Once a week try a steaming facial treatment – see method below – with two drops of lemon, two of juniper and two of tea tree. These oils will have a cleansing, detoxifying effect on the pores and prevent the blocking of the sebaceous glands.

GENERAL SPOTTINESS

The sebaceous glands in our skin produce sebum. This acts to naturally moisturize and protect skin. When these glands become overactive – sometimes due to hormonal changes – the sebum can become trapped beneath the skin. When the gland is blocked by this plug we have a blackhead. Blackheads that become infected turn into pimples. This infection can spread under the skin when we handle the skin or try to squeeze our spots. Squeezing them may also lead to scarring. Many medicated lotions and potions available from the chemist have strong antiseptic properties and can dry out and harm the skin while stopping the infection. Essential oils, however, are an excellent alternative, being both gentle and effective.

CLEANSING

Tea tree oil works amazingly quickly and effectively on spots. If you are prone to them start by using a good tea tree soap. Try to find a pure vegetable soap with two per cent pure tea tree oil. Daily use will prevent the blockage of the sebaceous glands and will not harm or dry out your skin. Tea tree is a powerful antiseptic but has a very low cineol content. This means it can do the job well without harming delicate skin. If you are not keen on soap – as I'm not – try a tea tree rinse. After your usual cleansing, half-fill your basin with water, add five drops of tea tree oil and rinse your face several times. You could even use both the soap and the rinse. Or perhaps use one in the morning and the other in the evening.

THE STEAM CLEAN

Once a week (maybe twice a week to begin with) try this deep-cleansing treament. Pour boiling water into a bowl and add three drops of tea tree, three of lavender, two of juniper and three of bergamot. Put a towel over your head, close your eyes and steam for about 10 minutes. The antiseptic, cleansing action of tea tree and juniper will draw any infection out. The lavender will soothe and begin to heal the skin and the bergamot will help to close the pores. When you have finished steaming your face, be sure to splash cold water on it several times to close the pores. Finally, cleanse and moisturize your skin.

THE TREATMENT OIL/CREAM

I prefer to use oil, rather than cream, on the skin. It is much easier to find pure carrier oils than creams and oils penetrate the layers of the skin much more effectively. For 50ml of carrier oil, blend together:

almond oil	25 ml
sunflower oil	20 ml
evening primrose oil	4 ml
Carrot oil	1 ml

and to this add:

lavender	9 drops
geranium	6 drops
bergamot	6 drops
tea tree	4 drops

If you prefer to use cream, try to buy the purest, simplest, most natural skin products possible, free from synthetic perfumes or ingredients. Mix the essential oils above, plus 1ml carrot oil and 1ml evening primrose oil, into 100g of cream.

After using this combination of oils for about three weeks, mix yourself the following blend:

almond oil	20 ml
sunflower oil	20 ml
evening primrose oil	5 ml
avocado oil	1 ml
wheatgerm oil	4 ml

and add to this:

lavender	10 ml
neroli	10 ml
geranium	5 ml

Once again, if you prefer using a cream, add the essential oils to the cream, plus, as before, 1ml carrot oil and 1ml primrose oil to 100g of the cream.

This second blend of essential oils will help to balance the sebum, reduce any scarring and encourage new skin growth.

For more skin potions see the section on beauty on pages 108–10.

PREGNANCY

This is a really good time to be under the care of an aromatherapist, as there are quite a few oils you should **not** use at this time. They are as follows:

angelica, birch, citronella, clary sage, rosemary, cypress, thyme, basil, geranium, hyssop, jasmine, fennel, marjoram, nutmeg, myrrh, peppermint, yarrow, cedarwood, rosemary, juniper, tarragon.

I must stress how important it is **not to use these oils.**

If you are unable to consult an aromatherapist, and are treating yourself, use essential oils (apart from those above) in greater dilution than usual and more sparingly. Always remember all oils are powerful and will affect you more at this time.

MORNING SICKNESS

As with all these symptoms, check with your doctor first before trying your own treatments. Two of my friends have used this recipe, devised by Valerie Ann Worwood, with excellent results. Place a bowl on the floor by your bed. Before

> *Another good remedy for morning sickness is ginger tea.*

you go to sleep, boil the kettle and pour boiling water into it. Add five drops of spearmint oil. Repeat this for three consecutive nights. Another good remedy for morning sickness is ginger tea.

OEDEMA

Try to rest with the legs higher than the head. Somehow, I always see my sister lying on the floor with her legs up a wall when I think of this. You can also try it on your couch or bed, with your legs supported and higher than your head. Try massaging your lower back and legs with this very dilute blend of oils. Always massage towards your heart and avoid the abdomen. Make up 50ml so you always have some ready for use.

To 50ml of carrier oil, add:

lavender	3 drops
ginger	4 drops
grapefruit	4 drops

Try to avoid salt, tea and coffee – they encourage the body to retain fluid. Nettle tea is said to be good for oedema – try one cup in the morning and one cup early evening.

The following recipes can apply after the birth too.

EXHAUSTION

Try the blend above in a foot bath, as a body oil or in a bath. Or try two drops of rose and one drop of lavender in a full bath or, diluted in two teaspoons of carrier oil, as a pick-me-up back rub.

VARICOSE VEINS

The recipe above will help to speed up the circulation and reduce the swelling in legs and ankles, so it may well prove helpful in treating varicose veins. It would be best to be under the guidance of your aromatherapist when using the alternative blend below.

To 50ml of carrier oil, add

geranium	15 drops
cypress	5 drops

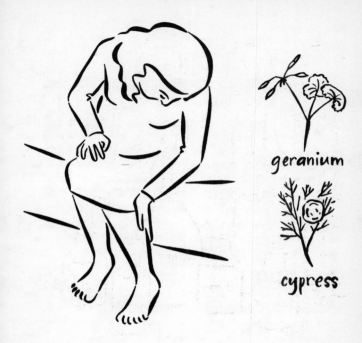

geranium

cypress

HAEMORRHOIDS

If you suffer from these, the blend above is very helpful for this complaint, too. I have also treated pregnant women who have found a simple mixture of two drops lavender in 10ml of carrier oil applied directly to the haemorrhoids soothing and totally effective.

STRETCHMARKS

The best idea is to begin a preventative treatment before they have a chance to form. From around the fourth to fifth month, try a daily massage of the entire abdomen, back and thighs with the blend below.

As a carrier oil, try a mixture of some of the following, until you have reached 50ml.

wheatgerm oil

borage oil

sunflower oil

rosehip seed oil

hazelnut oil

evening primrose oil

sweet almond oil

Borage oil and rosehip seed oil can be very difficult to find, but worth searching for. Hazelnut and sunflower oils are very rich in vitamin E which is great for skin. See what is available and experiment until you find what you like. Use only 10ml of wheatgerm and evening primrose in your blend. More of the other oils can be used – up to 50ml.

This recipe alone would make a difference to stretchmarks. However, for a super-effective blend, add to the carrier oil above sixteen drops of neroli and eight drops mandarin.

CHILDBIRTH

The most important thing in childbirth is that you are happy, as comfortable as possible and have your favourite smells around you. Many midwives are now conversant with oils for childbirth, so do take advantage of all their knowledge and experience.

Here are some ideas and a suggested plan for you to follow during this time. The oils are fairly interchangeable – what you like now may be quite different from what you fancy when you are actually in labour!

ONE WEEK PRIOR TO BIRTH:

To 10ml of carrier oil add five drops of rose. Apply this to the perineum daily. It helps to soften the area of muscle and tissue and prevent tearing during labour. Rose is also a uterine relaxant. It helps ligaments to soften thereby allowing the expansion of the pelvic bones. It is a good tonic for the heart, antiseptic and slightly analgesic in effect.

To 50ml of carrier oil add twenty drops of lavender. This is lovely for your daily bath, back rubs and massage during labour. Lavender is calming, good for headaches, slightly analgesic and stimulates the circulation. It is also anti-inflammatory and antiseptic.

> *Jasmine is effective in strengthening contractions, thus helping to shorten labour.*

To 50ml carrier oil add twenty drops jasmine. Jasmine is interchangeable with lavender for baths, back rubs and massage during labour. Jasmine is effective in strengthening contractions, thus helping to shorten labour. It is also good to use immediately after the birth to help deliver the afterbirth. It is a great anti-depressant and will help to tone the uterus after birth.

DELIVERY

Take, or ask someone to bring, your kit of the lavender blend or jasmine blend to the delivery room, just in case you really need them. I also recommend five drops of neroli to 10ml of carrier oil. This is a beautiful oil to use as a back rub during labour, for inhalation during the proceedings – either a few drops on a tissue or in a vaporizer. Neroli is beneficial to the nervous system and is deeply calming. It will increase oxygen supply to the brain and therefore tends to prevent hyperventilation. It is also antiseptic, anti-depressant and will restore confidence.

ESSENTIAL OILS BIRTH PLAN

I would begin by vaporizing three to four drops of lavender oil on an oil burner. Use jasmine and clary sage to strengthen the contractions at the midwife's instruction – clary sage can also be quite euphoric. Inhale these directly, vaporize them or go for the back massage with the jasmine blend. Only at the time will you know what is best – another airing for the intuition! Remember that jasmine can help to deliver the afterbirth. However, jasmine can be very heavy in the air, so I suggest burning it with lavender which is fresh and clean smelling in comparison.

These same oils are lovely in the post-natal period too for baths, massages and vaporizing. Neroli, clary sage and jasmine are all helpful for those post-natal blues.

PMT AND HRT

As well as providing some practical, easy help for the lunar afflicted, this section is also really good for those men who may wish to 'survive' such occurrences!

YOUR CYCLE

It you have real problem periods or any medical condition, seek professional help and advice before trying anything here. Then, when you know what you are dealing with, it is worth spending some time with an aromatherapist and finding out exactly what helps *you*. Essential oils can be life-changing for menstrual cycle problems. We spend thirty to forty years in this monthly cycle, so treatment with oils is a worthwhile investment.

Essential oils can be life-changing for menstrual cycle problems.

Take time to get to know your body better. After your next period – the first day of bleeding is day one of your cycle – spend a few minutes daily in the bath or shower noticing your body and checking how you feel. You will gain an understanding of the changes of *your* body. After all, we are all slightly different.

ERRATIC, PAINFUL OR HEAVY PERIODS

Try this general regime:

Day four to day fourteen: rub the entire abdomen, small of back and the hips daily with 30ml of carrier oil, with the following added:

clary sage	5 drops
geranium	5 drops
chamomile	5 drops

Mix enough in advance so it is ready to use every day and store in an amber bottle. The oils work better when mixed 'together' this way.

Day fifteen to day twenty-eight: follow the same method but with this blend:

juniper	5 drops
bergamot	5 drops
lavender	5 drops

Evening primrose oil or the herb agnus castus can also be helpful during these two weeks. Nutrition plays its part too as always, so reduce your intake of tea, coffee and cigarettes. You may benfit from a course of vitamin B complex or B6. Use your intuition. Read about them, have a look at them, try them. Don't be shy to say, no, this isn't for me. Listen to your body, see what it responds to.

EXTREMELY HEAVY PERIODS:

Days fifteen to day twenty-eight: try the following:

To 30ml of carrier oil, add

cypress	5 drops
geranium	5 drops
lavender	5 drops

Rose oil may be used instead of geranium in this blend. Rose is a lovely oil to use in the latter part of the cycle. I haven't included it generally as it is very expensive and I am mindful of our budgets! However

> *Rose is a wonderful uterine tonic and can have a regulating effect on the menstrual cycle*

rose is a wonderful uterine tonic and can have a regulating effect on the menstrual cycle. If you add five drops of this essential oil, remember to add 10 ml more of carrier oil.

If you have heavy periods *avoid* clary sage or sage in the latter part of your cycle. Both of these can increase the bleeding even though they are good anti-spasmodics and work well for cramps.

FLUID RETENTION

Lymphatic drainage massage can be really valuable here, working with your aromatherapist and oils of rosemary, juniper, cypress, grapefruit and geranium. I recommend weekly massages for the first three to four weeks and then once a month.

HEADACHES

Try applying a little neat lavender to the temples and the back of the neck. This can of course be done anywhere, which is a great advantage! When at home try two drops of lavender with two of peppermint in a small bowl of warm water. Wet a flannel in the water, wring it out and use as a compress across the forehead and/or on the back of the neck. If you are also feeling quite emotional add a drop of chamomile to the water before using the compress.

SPOTS

For those red lumpy spots dab on a neat drop of tea tree morning and night. You will find they go very quickly.

If your pre-menstrual experience is not so physical in nature, but tends to alter your behaviour, try one of the blends below, either in your bath or as a daily massage over the abdomen, small of the back, hips and tail bone. Whatever symptoms you have during your cycle, one thing I recommend is walking. Take yourself out for a brisk walk. It is simple tonic and great for general well being.

NEGATIVE MOODS

If you become totally disagreeable try two drops of geranium, two of clary sage and two of bergamot in your bath. Or blend in a 50ml amber/blue bottle of carrier oil seven drops of geranium, seven of clary sage and seven of bergamot to use as a body or bath oil – but only during this time.

THE 'WEEPIES'

If this tends to happen to you, try two drops of rose, three of clary sage and two of bergamot in your bath. Or in an amber/blue 50ml bottle of carrier oil blend seven drops of rose, seven of bergamot and ten of clary sage.

THE 'WHATEVERS'

If you tend to feel apathetic and listless try adding two drops of geranium, two of clary sage and two of grapefruit to your bath on these days. Alternatively, blend in a 50ml amber/blue bottle of carrier oil seven drops of geranium, seven of clary sage and seven of grapefruit and use as a body or bath oil for this time of the month.

THE 'AGGRESSIVES'

If latent aggression rears its ever-so-ugly-head at this time, then try adding four drops of geranium, two drops chamomile and two drops of bergamot to your baths at this time of the month. Or with 50ml of carrier oil in an amber or blue bottle mix twelve drops of geranium, six drops of chamomile and six drops of bergamot to use over these days as a body or bath oil.

In whichever category you classify yourself, try a fragrant and therapeutic bath. Remember always to run your bath first then add the oils.

MENOPAUSE

This is the time when the process of menstruating ceases. It may take months or several years in some people and can be physically and emotionally uncomfortable. Every woman experiences this time differently and it is difficult to find patterns into which I can neatly slot my recipes.

The menopause is a good time to assess your own general health. Again I would recommed a trip to your doctor for a check-up. Are you taking regular exercise? Are you eating a healthy diet, with a broad range of foods? Would it be wise to try a supplement such as evening primrose oil? Here are some of the oils that may help you with the symptoms of menopause as you go through this transition.

ANTI-DEPRESSANTS

All the anti-depressant oils are valuable at this time: bergamot, clary sage, jasmine, lavender, neroli, sandalwood, ylang-ylang and rose.

HEAVY PERIODS

For excessively heavy periods at this time, see the PMT section (page 60) and bear in mind that other problems, such as fibroids, may cause this. I cannot stress how important it is to know exactly what you are dealing with before using oils, so get anything suspect checked out.

HOT FLUSHES

Blend the following in 10ml of carrier oil:

lemon	1 drop
clary sage	2 drops
geranium	2 drops

Add to your bath. You may also make up more of the mixture and keep it in a blue/amber bottle to use as a body oil. Massage daily into your abdomen, hips and lower back.

Evening primrose oil is reported to be very effective in treating hot flushes so it may be well worth trying a course in combination with the oils.

SWEATS

Blend in 10ml of carrier oil:

grapefruit	2 drops
lime	1 drop
geranium	2 drops

Add to your bath. You may also make up more of the mixture and keep it in a blue/amber bottle to use as a body oil. Massage daily into your abdomen, hips and lower back.

BLOATING

Blend in 10ml of carrier oil:

fennel	2 drops
juniper	2 drops
grapefruit	1 drop

Add to your bath. Make up more of the mixture and keep it in a blue/amber bottle to use as a body oil. Massage daily into your abdomen, hips and lower back.

CIRCULATION PROBLEMS

Blend in 10ml of carrier oil:

geranium	2 drops
peppermint	1 drop
rose	2 drops

Add to your bath. You can also make up more of the mixture and keep it in a blue/amber bottle to use as a body oil. Massage daily into your abdomen, hips and lower back. This is also a good mixture to rub into the legs. Always remember to work upwards from the feet, towards the heart, to encourage the return of the blood to the heart. If you are sitting down put your feet up higher than the level of your heart. Lying on your bed with your feet up the wall works really well.

Good luck! If it all seems too much on some days have a peek in the Stress Relievers section (see pages 26–8). Above all, remember that 'this too shall pass'. It is a transition you are going through – not the end!

ABOUT THE HOUSE

Our homes are the scene of so much activity. Sometimes it really does seem that the work is never ending! When you absolutely *have* to do the washing or cleaning, but really do feel too tired, try using essential oils in one of the following ways – you'll find they really give you a lift!

*When you absolutely **have** to do the washing or cleaning, but really do feel too tired, try using essential oils*

Most essential oils are antiseptic and/or bactericidal. This makes them ideal for cleaning as they inhibit the growth of bacteria. Not only do they make the environment cleaner, but they smell great as well and really give you a lift!

CLEANING

Washing up: dishwashing liquids all seem to have lemon in them. Why not try using natural lemon? Whatever liquid you use try adding a total of ten drops of lime, lemon, grapefruit or bergamot per 500ml of liquid. Then the oils can be doing their bit with their uplifting qualities while you are slaving away. You'll probably end up feeling better for doing the dishes – but don't tell anyone!

General cleaning: a couple of drops of lavender, lemon, eucalyptus, lime, bergamot, pine, lemongrass or thyme is a good addition to any cleaning activity. For benches, sinks, wood floors, fridges or paintwork, add one or two drops directly to a cloth or about eight drops to the rinse water for larger areas. There will be no horrible chemical smell – these oils are natural and effective. There is now so much literature supporting the bactericidal effectiveness of natural oils – in fact in many products the natural ingredients are the effective ingredients. The chemicals are only necessary because we believe that's what's needed.

> *In many products the natural ingredients are the effective ingredients*

Spring cleaning the bathroom: add thyme to the water you use to wash down and rinse the ceiling and walls. Thyme works well to prevent mould growing in these moist conditions.

Cleaning the rubbish bin: add a couple of drops of thyme, eucalyptus or tea tree to the water.

Vacuuming: add a drop or two of thyme, eucalyptus or tea tree to your vacuum cleaner bag or add drops to a cotton wool ball and pop that in the vacuum cleaner bag.

In the dishwasher: try adding a couple of drops of lemon, lemongrass, lime or grapefruit to the dishwasher salt.

Down the drains: pour a few drops of your old essential oil down the drains. The oils will still be slightly bactericidal and antiseptic and the drains will certainly smell better.

WASHING

For washing, I recommend the clearer, more watery oils, such as lavender, rosemary, lemon, bergamot, lemongrass, orange, petitgrain or geranium. If everyone in the house has a cold, try adding a few drops of eucalyptus or pine to your washing.

General clothes washing: if you want your clothes to smell good after washing, try adding, to a full wash, about five drops of essential oil in with the fabric conditioner.

For hand-washing: try just a couple of drops in the final rinse.

For clothes in a tumble-dryer: put three to four drops of one of the oils above on a piece of fabric and pop this in with the clothes. Or you could try drying pyjamas with drops of lavender and chamomile to help induce sleep, or eucalyptus or tea tree when there are colds and flu about.

try drying pyjamas with drops of lavender and chamomile to help induce sleep

For smelly trainers: if they are machine washable put drops of tea tree, rosemary and eucalyptus in their wash. Or you could add two drops of eucalyptus or tea tree to a tablespoon of bicarbonate of soda.

Mix this and drop into the shoes overnight. This can make a huge difference to everyone's life!

For anything that needs soaking before washing – tea towels, sports gear, tablecloths: drops of thyme, eucalyptus, lavender or tea tree are excellent for disinfecting. Do not use more than a total of five drops when soaking.

For sticky, tar-like stains on clothes: try eucalyptus. It can be used directly on most fabrics without harming them. With cotton fabrics, just drop eucalyptus onto the stain and add to the wash. Or try soaking a cotton bud in the oil and lifting the stain from the garment. It might be wise to test a piece of a more delicate fabric first.

For chewing gum: put the whole garment in the freezer for a few minutes to harden the chewing gum and the garment. Dab on the eucalyptus, easing it between the gum and garment and just lift the chewing gum off.

IRONING

Add two drops of your favourite oil to 200ml of water in the plant spray and give your clothes a quick spray before ironing.

STORAGE

For those old, past their sell-by date essential oils there is another use. Drop the oils on cotton wool balls and pop them in the airing cupboard. Alternatively, add your choice of oils to an old piece of fabric and hang it down the side of the hot water tank. The whole cupboard will become fragrant. You can also try this in drawers and clothes cupboards.

Drawer liners: try making your own drawer liners using pieces of unused wallpaper. Cut the paper into the size required for each drawer and add a few drops of your favourite oils or anti-moth blend. Tried and tested moth repellents are camphor, patchouli, lavender, lemongrass, citronella, thyme and rosemary. You can try these on their own, or blend two you like together. You could try keeping your pyjamas in a lavender- and chamomile-smelling drawer. Rosemary and grapefruit are a perfect combination for scenting drawers filled with workwear and schoolwear. Jasmine and ylang-ylang are wonderful for lingerie.

FRAGRANCING

As room sprays are very easy to make with essential oils, there is no real need to use the chemical varieties. Use a small plant spray and add about four drops of oil per 200ml of water – there is no need to make them any stronger. You can make individual aromas for different occasions and different rooms in your house.

For the kitchen: try a mixture of rosemary, lemon, lime and eucalyptus, for some of those hard to get rid of and not so pleasant kitchen aromas.

The living-room: this room requires a different mixture, perhaps cedarwood, geranium, orange, sandalwood. A blend of these oils is warm and welcoming. In the winter you may like to try a few drops of sandalwood or cedarwood on your fire wood. Either of these will generate a beautiful, real wood aroma from the fire and throughout the room. Make sure the oil has time to dry before you burn it.

> *In the winter you may like to try a few drops of sandalwood or cedarwood on your fire wood.*

A sick room: would benefit from a spray of tea tree, lemon, lavender, eucalyptus. This is so easy to make and guaranteed to make everyone feel better!

You could make a different blend for any occasion. Remember to give the spray a good shake before you use it. Always hold the spray six to eight inches away from furnishings, curtains and carpets, which will hold the fragrance best. Try to avoid directing towards delicate fabrics.

POT POURRI

Many natural materials absorb fragrant oils. Get creative and experiment with pieces of wood, bark and stones in your home – all these are perfect for scenting with essential oils. Fruit stones are especially interesting 'holders of fragrance'. Or you could try the more usual dried flowers. A friend of mine always has cut flowers in her house. When these flowers are on their way out she dries them, no matter what they are. Some of these flower heads and leaves are really beautiful and they make a wonderful, and unusual, pot pourri.

It's a good idea to make pot pourri and room sprays that go together and using the same or complementary oils in a vaporizer or diffuser adds to the atmosphere. You could make a room spray with two drops lemon, one of orange and one of rosemary. The 'matching' pot pourri could have, say, three drops of lemon, two of orange and one of rosemary. Seal the pot pourri in a plastic bag for a couple of days prior to use. While you are waiting to use it, try various blends with orange, lemon and rosemary on a diffuser. During celebrations, birthdays, Easter and Christmas it might be fun to co-ordinate your aromas – even though they may be subtle, aromas make a lasting impression on the memory and can help people remember events.

TRAVELLING

I always put together a travel kit of oils. Once you've travelled with one, you'll wonder how you ever managed without one – it becomes indispensable. When I want to travel lightly, I make sure I always take lavender, chamomile, tea tree, geranium, ginger and either peppermint or lemongrass. I would probably take grapefruit, too, and neroli, my favourite oil. You may have other favourites.

As a quick reference, here is a guide to the uses of oils on your travels. There may well be other oils you want to add to your own personal travel kit. Modify it to suit you.

LAVENDER AND CHAMOMILE

Essential for burns, blisters, bites, bruises, heatstroke, prickly heat and rashes, to help you sleep, for sunburn and windburn, dry skin, exhaustion, sprains and strains.

GERANIUM

Handy for blisters, exhaustion, muscle cramps, bruises and dry skin. Treat exposure to cold in conjunction with ginger. It is also great for adjusting to time zones.

TEA TREE

Excellent for bites, colds, cuts and scratches, infections, itching, inflammation. Combine with lavender to treat sunstroke.

GINGER

For chills, exposure to cold, indigestion, travel sickness. Treat upset tummy in conjunction with lavender or peppermint.

PEPPERMINT

Soothes upset tummy, headaches, toothache, insect repellent, indigestion, constipation. Can be used as an insect repellent and general pick-me-up.

LEMONGRASS

Acts as an insect repellent.

IF YOU HATE TRAVELLING

For those of you who hate travelling, but have to do it, try a bath with two drops of rosemary, two of geranium and two of orange before you venture onto your bus, boat, car or aeroplane. The same drops on a tissue to inhale would be a good travelling companion. If you have to drive a lot, carry a small bottle of rosemary or peppermint essential oil in the car. Sometimes, even with regular breaks, just inhaling the oil can help to clear your head and keep you alert.

Travel sickness

Peppermint is very calming for the stomach and has the added bonus of increasing mental alertness. For these reasons it's a good travellers' oil. Ginger is another oil well known for easing nausea and sickness. With either of these oils try a couple of drops on a tissue to inhale and tuck the tissue into the top pocket of your shirt so the smells will waft 'nosewards' while

> *Peppermint is very calming for the stomach and has the added bonus of increasing mental alertness.*

you are on your journey. You could also try a couple of drops of your preferred oil on a cotton wool ball. Put this on the dashboard out of the way but where the smells will still permeate the car. If you or your children are prone to travel sickness, start inhaling the oils an hour before your journey and drink some ginger or peppermint tea, too.

TRAVELLING ON A BUDGET

Take it from one who knows: essential oils are totally essential when travelling on a budget – unless you really like to punish yourself, that is! When you are not sure of the cleanliness of some of the places you will be staying, carrying the oils suggested at the beginning of this section will give you some peace of mind. On a dodgy mattress sprinkle a few drops of tea tree and/or lavender. I sometimes add a couple of drops of lemongrass too. Any of these will help and allow you to get at least a little sleep. I always carry two sarong-type pieces of fabric with me. I first used one of these when I was thirteen, in Indonesia. After mastering several ways to tie them so they stay on I've never been without them. You can use these to sleep on (after treating your mattress), to sit on, on top of your rucksack – which tends to get filthy while travelling – while you are waiting for transport. They are handy for sunbathing on and very comfortable to wear in the heat, or after your shower. They can be washed in water with a drop of tea tree to disinfect them, and they dry very quickly. Bathrooms can feel very unclean in

> *On a dodgy mattress sprinkle a few drops of tea tree and/or lavender.*

some places. If they have bench surfaces and toilet seats you will feel better about using them if you've cleaned them first with tea tree. Add twenty drops to a glass of water and pour over the surfaces. Wipe down with toilet paper or wet wipes if you can. If your bathroom is the 'hole in the floor' type, just sluice the entire area with this same mixture.

After treating your mattress, it may help to make you feel more secure if you sprinkle a few drops of oil around your bed space to discourage creepy crawlies. Lemongrass, peppermint and/or lavender are good for this. You could fill a bowl or two with boiling water and add a few drops of these oils. Put drops on cotton wool and place them strategically around the room. I've even put them on one of my fabrics and flown it as a flag in the evening so we could eat in peace! Be inventive!

FACING THE PUBLIC

If you are travelling abroad and have an important meeting to attend, or you've been working on a project and now have to present it overseas, you need to be at your best, and this can be a challenge after a long flight. Give yourself a head start and drink plenty of water and little or no alcohol. Fly with a bottle of lavender handy – put some on a tissue to inhale from time to time to relax you. If you are feeling a bit anxious, try lavender on your pulse points and on the soles of your feet. I usually travel with a small bottle of blended lavender (five drops of lavender in 10ml of carrier oil). Mix up your own blend and try giving yourself a foot massage on the plane. You may find you end up having a nice snooze! Add a drop of chamomile to this blend if you are feeling anxious and frazzled.

When you get to the other end, try not to sleep at your usual time, but adapt to the time change and get your body clock accustomed to it. Use your oils to help you. To prepare for your meeting or presentation, begin with a morning bath of three drops of lavender and three of grapefruit. When you are preparing this bath, put one drop of each of these oils onto a tissue to carry with you. This simple blend will work wonders. Other oils you can substitute are rosemary and geranium. These may be used with lavender or in a blend of their own: in a bath, three drops of geranium and two of rosemary.

Experiment and discover the oils that suit you. Keep your oils to hand and always remember them when you travel.

> *To prepare for your meeting or presentation, begin with a morning bath of three drops of lavender and three of grapefruit.*

SUNCARE

PREPARATION

If you know you're going to be exposing your body to the sun's rays on holiday then it is a good idea to prepare for it. Dry skin brushing is the first treatment. This helps your body get rid of all the old skin cells, so that the younger skin can breathe feely. You will need a natural bristle body brush. Use it daily, always brushing your skin in the direction of your heart. This process not only exfoliates – takes those dead skin cells away – but also stimulates the circulation so that the skin is well nourished by a good blood supply. It's a good idea to use a body moisturizer a couple of times a week at least, especially if you work in artificially heated/cooled environments a lot. I always bathe using oils – it's the lazy way to moisturize your body and, I think, the most enjoyable. The process of looking after the body in this way can also help

> *I always bathe using oils – it's the lazy way to moisturize your body and, I think, the most enjoyable.*

to make us more aware of our bodies, so keep an eye on the texture and colour of your skin while you take care of it. Drinking plenty of water and taking extra vitamin C will help your skin cope better with the sudden exposure to different weather and the sun's rays.

WHILE YOU'RE THERE

While it is a lovely feeling to have the sun on your skin, be mindful. There are so many warnings now about skin cancer and how it's at least partly caused by exposure to the sun, yet people still spend hours lying on the beach. If you love to lie in the sun, just increase your awareness of moles and patches on your skin. If you see a new mole don't panic about it – just keep your eye on it. Patches or moles that change dramatically in colour and/or shape, or others that just don't heal properly if they have been knocked, should be investigated. Caught early, these will not become a problem. For those parts of you you can't see, ask the person putting on your sunscreen to look for you. If you haven't been in the sun for a year or more and suddenly go to a hot spot, remember that our world is changing and the holes in the ozone layer dramatically affect the strength of the sun. Last time I was in New Zealand, after a couple of English summers, I thought I was being very moderate only having fifteen minutes in the mid-morning sun. I was shocked that I burned so much so quickly – fortunately, I was saved by lavender! Just be careful.

The best times to expose yourself to the sun are early morning and late afternoon. Copy the natives in most sunny places and retreat to a cool place at midday. Always remember to apply a sunscreen when you are in the sun and reapply after swimming.

Treatment for burns

Lavender is simply amazing for burns, although tea tree can be a good back-up if there is no lavender to hand. Lavender can be applied neat to all minor burns including sunburn. If this is done very soon after burning you will not get blisters or even scars. Reapply regularly – every two hours – over a twenty-four hour period. Lavender also acts as a very effective antiseptic and

> *Lavender can
> be applied neat
> to all minor burns
> including sunburn.*

pain killer. It will help to reduce swelling and promote rapid healing. I use hot wax in the finishing of my products and always have a bottle of lavender close by. My hands are testament to the efficiency of lavender with burns. For the number of times they have been burned with hot wax, only one tiny scar remains and that was because I forgot apply lavender for the first twenty-four hours.

Chamomile

The two most commonly used types of chamomile are Roman chamomile (*Anthemis nobilis*) and German chamomile (*Matricaria chamomilla*). Their properties are very similar. German chamomile contains mainly farnesene and chamazulene. Roman chamomile is made up of esters (angelic ester, tiglic ester) isobutyl angelate, chamazulene and pinocarvone. The chamazulene is not found in the actual plant but is naturally produced during steam distillation. This is responsible for the lovely blue colour and the excellent anti-inflammatory properties of the oil. Both chamomiles are soothing and calming in every sense. Chamomile tea has for centuries been used for these very properties. Hot compresses were used for boils and abcesses (even tooth abcesses), infected wounds and cuts. For internal inflammatory conditions it can help to take chamomile tea while undergoing treatment with chamomile oil.

> *Skin problems respond
> to chamomile's soothing
> touch, especially where
> there is inflammation,
> redness and dryness.*

With conditions of the digestive system such as gastritis and colitis, where tension and anxiety play a noted part, chamomile's soothing, calming qualities can work exceptionally well. Skin problems respond to chamomile's soothing touch, especially where there is inflammation, redness and dryness. That's why it works so well with sunburn. Blended with lavender, these two oils work wonders with the burning, as one supports the other.

Being a very gentle oil, chamomile is suitable for the frail and fragile and children, and soothes nervousness. With some people, I have found it can dramatically reduce stress or anxiety in ways that other oils cannot.

Treatment for burns with lavender and chamomile As soon as you realize your skin is burned apply neat lavender to prevent blistering and scarring and keep out of the sun. Soak yourself in a coolish bath with four drops of lavender and three drops of chamomile. Then mix yourself the following oil to use over the next couple of days to treat your skin with:

In 50 ml of carrier oil add:

lavender	15 drops
chamomile	8 drops

You could also try adding one or two drops of bergamot as this will help to retain your tan. Make sure you don't apply bergamot *before* going in the sun. It makes the skin more sensitive and will make it burn even more. Just take care with those rays!

TREATING THE FEET

Feet get a tough time from most of us, don't they? We expect a lot from them and don't really look after them the way we should. Feet are actually the one part of our body from which we reap rewards when we do give them attention. They contain 72,000 nerve endings from pathways all over the body. A foot massage is a mini body massage. The effects permeate the entire body.

When our feet just aren't right the repercussions are felt throughout our system. When their balance is altered, then our walk changes and we may suffer from back strain, neck strain and other ailments – all resulting from our feet!

Feet are also our connection with the earth. When we go barefoot on sand, in the sea or on summer grass we tend to feel more connected to all life. Our electricity and the earth's link up.

GENERAL FOOT FITNESS

Allow your feet room in your shoes. Ensure you can spread your toes. Walk *through* your feet – work every part of your foot with each step. When I've experienced problems with my back, I've taken myself walking and made myself *use* my feet with each step. If you do this consciously for a while you'll find it becomes a habit. Stretch your feet and spread your toes and breathe deeply. I found this did my back a power of good. If you walk to the station or down to the shops try 'conscious walking' to exercise your feet. You will find other parts of you benefit too!

Hard skin
If this is allowed to build up it may cause discomfort at a later date. It's a good idea to look after the skin on your feet and keep the tough skin to a minimum. Blisters under hard skin can be incredibly painful. You may need to use a softening cream once or twice a week to help shift it. To make your own skin softener, add four drops of lavender, three drops of lemon and three drops of benzoin to 50g of unperfumed cream. If you can find a cream with vitamin E in it, so much the better. Coarse salt rubbed into the feet is a pleasant dry skin remover. I also recommend pumice which I used to collect from the beach when I was a child. It is excellent for keeping your feet soft. I have recently discovered a marvellous clay foot scrub and this is my present favourite. Experiment with different methods and see what works for you. Try something like this at least once a week.

Reflexology
If you ever get the opportunity, try reflexology. It's a lovely treat for the whole body, not just the feet. I love it because I love my feet being touched – and I get to have a rest! I know many people who have been surprised by how effective it is. If you're shy, just remember: it's only your shoes and socks that have to come off!

Foot baths

A simple do-it-yourself treat! Here are a few ideas and some background on an oil that's a real tonic for your feet.

Ginger Ginger (*Zingiber officinalis*) is a native of the East and was originally brought to England along the spice route. It is now grown in Africa, the West Indies and South America, as well as China and India. The essential oil comes from the root of the ginger plant and is produced by steam distillation. The main chemical constituents are gingerin, gingenol, gingerone and zingiberine.

> *This oil can help with nausea, both morning sickness and travel sickness. It is also excellent in a gargle when treating sore throats.*

From ancient times the uses of ginger have been both culinary and medicinal. In Chinese medicine ginger is used when the body is not coping with moisture in some way. Colds and rheumatism are examples of the kind of moisture from 'outside', whereas catarrh and diarrhoea are examples of it 'inside' the body. In each case the balance of moisture is not correct and ginger is used to redress this balance.

Ginger is also used as a tonic, especially in autumn. For colds and flu, ginger is warming as a tea and helps counteract these winter ailments. In any massage blend it must be less concentrated than most oils or it may irritate the skin.

This oil can help with nausea, both morning sickness and travel sickness. It is also excellent in a gargle when treating sore throats.

Ginger foot bath Although peppermint oil is traditionally used for feet as it is so refreshing, ginger is a good alternative as it stimulates and strengthens the whole body. This makes a good autumn/winter foot bath: fill your basin with warm water and add just two or three drops of ginger essential oil. You can use two drops of peppermint with one drop of ginger instead or one drop each of ginger and orange oil.

Foot bath for tired or aching feet Try this old English remedy: pour a litre of boiling water over about 50g of fresh marigold leaves. Cover and leave to cool. Strain this into your warm foot bath and soak for a good ten minutes. Try this with lavender flowers too.

Mustard foot bath The first time I saw ground mustard I thought it was a special kind of bath salts and promptly had a bath in them – not recommended! My Scottish grandmother soon sorted me out. Put about one cupful of ground mustard in a pan with just enough water to cover it. Boil this for about ten minutes. Add to your warm foot bath. This is great for colds and flu time.

Like a bath, you can use whichever oils you choose in a foot bath. Make it relaxing with geranium. Try peppermint to prepare your feet for lots of walking.

Pampering your feet One of the places I went on holiday as a child was called Hot Water Beach. There we would dig in the sand and sit in the hot water that came up through the sand. We used to try and keep our little bath intact by building low sand walls and lining the floor with stones and rocks. We never succeeded as the tide would always come in and sand would always fill our hot bath up again the next day! What I enjoyed most was the feeling of the rocks and stones beneath my feet in the hot bath. Why not try this in your own home? Collect a few smooth and pumice-type stones and try them in your foot bath. Roll your feet around them and let the stones give your feet a good masage. I think this is even better than a do-it-yourself foot massage.

HANGOVER CURES

These pages contain the results of a great deal of scientific study. I had no lack of volunteers for my 'hangover trial' to test my aromatic troubleshooting!

Out of all the oils experimented with, a combination of fennel, geranium and juniper seemed to work best.

FENNEL

The oil is distilled from the seeds of the plant and exudes a sweet, aniseed aroma – the plant comes from the same family as aniseed. The oil contains camphene, estragol, fenchone, anethol and phellandrene. Fennel is a tonic for the digestive system and deals quickly with nausea. It also seems to strengthen the contractions of the intestinal muscles. A good diuretic, fennel helps the body cleanse itself and is particularly effective in expelling alcohol. Fennel must not be used by children under twelve years, epileptics, during pregnancy or by those with high oestrogen levels.

> *Fennel is a tonic for the digestive system and deals quickly with nausea.*

GERANIUM

Distilled from the leaves of the plant, geranium oil smells fragrant, as though it has been extracted from the flowers. The plant used is not the same as the ones found in our gardens here but one of two hundred varieties that come from the Mediterranean and Africa. The main chemical constituents of geranium are geraniol and citronellol. It is a balancing oil and can be both uplifting or sedative, depending on the amount used. It is valuable for general elimination and a tonic for the liver and kidneys.

JUNIPER

The best juniper oil is steam distilled from the berries and contains camphor of juniper, alpha pinene, cadinene, camphene, terpineol and borneol. With its diruretic and antiseptic properties, juniper is excellent where detoxification is required. It can help in various part of the body where poor elimination is a problem. Juniper has also been used for centuries as a protection from infection.

Do not use in pregnancy, on children under twelve years or for those with kidney problems.

THE CURE

If you don't have to work the day after heavy drinking, sleep, as ever, is the best healer. Combine as much sleep as possible with lots of pure water and some extra vitamin C – both of these can work if taken the night before. For those who must work, the combination of these oils will clear your head, take away that fragile feeling and stimulate your body's own detoxification process.

The bath
Fill a bath, add two drops of fennel, four drops of geranium and one drop of juniper and have a good soak for at least ten minutes. Mix these three oils with two teaspoons of pure vegetable oil in a little dish so you have some ready for inhalation later on.

> *For those who must work, the combination of these oils will clear your head, take away that fragile feeling and stimulate your body's own detoxification process.*

The rub

After a shower, wet a flannel and wring it out. Drop the same amount of fennel, geranium and juniper as above onto the flannel and give yourself a vigorous rub down. I like this with two drops of grapefruit oil added.

Mobile cure

Before you leave the house, rub some of the reserved mix you made up for your bath on the backs of your hands and/or on a tissue to take with you.

We are all different and you may not like this combination of oils – if not, they are probably not the best ones for you! If that is the case, try:

Fennel, juniper and rosemary: combine three drops of fennel with two drops of juniper and three of rosemary to a full bath. Or, combine one drop of each in one teaspoon of pure vegetable oil, add to a tissue and inhale as you go about your day.

Lavender and peppermint: Add four drops of lavender and three of peppermint to your bath and soak for ten minutes. Or, drop three of each onto a damp flannel and rub yourself down after a morning shower.

Geranium and lemon: Add four drops of geranium and two drops of lemon to a full bath (always go easy on the citrus oils as they can irritate your skin). Or, use three drops of geranium and one of lemon in a teaspoon of carrier oil and rub on the back of your hands to smell as you travel to work and during the day.

MONDAY MORNINGS

Who doesn't need help with Monday mornings? Let's look at some of the beautifully uplifting essential oils that help launch us into the week without the groaning. Choose from lavender, geranium, rosemary, lemongrass and grapefruit. It is a good idea to vary the oils you use and try – even if you

> *Who doesn't need help with Monday mornings? Let's look at some of the beautifully uplifting essential oils that help launch us into the week without the groaning.*

are sleepy – to let your intuition guide you. See what oils your hands go for and, if they feel right, just go ahead and use them – they are usually perfect. Before I suggest a few blends to try, let me give you a profile of lemongrass.

LEMONGRASS

Lemongrass is a scented grass native to India. It has strong antiseptic and bactericidal properties and for these reasons has been used in Indian medicine for thousands of years to fight infectious diseases and fevers. The reason it is a good Monday morning oil is its stimulating effect on the whole system. It is a great 'tonic' of an oil. Like other citrus oils, lemongrass can irritate the skin so it needs to be used in a very dilute form.

The chemical constituents of most varieties of lemongrass are citral (about seventy per cent), geraniol, farnesol, citonellol, myrcene, nerol and aldehydes. The grass grows to about three feet high and several crops can be taken in one season. The oil is extracted by steam distillation.

Refreshing and deodorizing both describe lemongrass. From experience it is also lovely in a footbath. This oil is very effective with sweaty feet, as it seems to help balance the oil production in the feet. It will deodorize quite naturally as well – it's well worth taking on holiday!

While lemongrass is a tonic for the whole body and feels like a stimulant, it seems to have a sedative effect on the central nervous system. For Monday mornings this is perfect. You can be woken and enlivened, yet not set buzzing!

If you have a headache and there is no lavender available, lemongrass can have a very soothing effect. Just remember lemongrass needs diluting before you apply it to your temples, forehead and top of your neck (where you head joins your neck).

Again, like other citrus oils, lemongrass is a good insect repellent. It can be vaporized on a burner to keep flies and mosquitoes away and can help pets with their flea problems. Quite a versatile oil!

So, when you take your morning bath, try one of these blends:

either		*or*	
lavender	3 drops	lavender	2 drops
geranium	2 drops	rosemary	1 drop
lemongrass	2 drops	grapefruit	2 drops

Remember always to fill your bath first before adding your oils.

Remember always to fill your bath first before adding your oils.

You can also drop the same quantities of oil on a warm, wet flannel and give your body a brisk rub down after your shower or, as one friend of mine likes to do, while you are in the shower.

ROSEMARY

This is another oil with a long history of medicinal use. The plant is native to the Mediterranean. The essential oil is steam distilled and has a sharp, permeating aroma. In history it was often referred to as the incense bush. In many Mediterranean countries rosemary was burned on shrines and in sacred places. It was also used for performing exorcisms and burned in sickrooms and hospitals.

Rosemary has the ability to clear the head. This has been documented from as far back as the Roman era. This works on a physical level – it is great for colds, catarrh and sinus problems and, on a mental level, it is a good brain stimulant.

The chemical constituents of rosemary are camphor, pinene, borneol, cineol but it can vary quite a bit in its chemistry from variety to variety.

Rosemary is a heart tonic and circulatory stimulant. It promotes general circulation and in particular stimulates the blood supply to the brain. Therefore it can help relieve mental fatigue, fainting and seems to improve the memory.

The general tonic effect of rosemary works on the emotions as well and this is another reason why it is a good choice for a Monday morning bath. It dispels lethargy and apathy.

Blend yourself a Monday morning mix to use on any day of the week when you need a little extra help.

To 50ml of carrier oil add:

either		*or*	
rosemary	8 drops	lavender	10 drops
geranium	10 drops	geranium	8 drops
orange	8 drops	lemongrass	8 drops

I am always surprised at how wonderful these essential oils are. We all need input and support in daily life and these beautiful tools are an incredible way of helping yourself. So when you need help starting the day, don't think, as I used to all the time, 'I should be fine, I shouldn't need help.' Help yourself, with the oils, to get through the day. I believe that when we begin to help and support ourselves, the world begins to help and support us too.

MEN ONLY

This section is just for you. You often get left out when health and beauty matters are discussed. Perhaps when remedies sound all too complicated you just give up! The problems mentioned here are the ones you might not like to talk about but they can make daily life very uncomfortable. The remedies are remarkably simple, natural, quick and very effective.

SHAVING CUTS

A 10ml bottle of lavender is the best thing to have in the house for these. Put a couple of drops onto your finger and apply neat to the cut. You could try reading the section on lavender on page 16 – it's such a useful oil to have about the house and can be used for burns, headaches and helping you sleep. Invest in a bottle.

lavender

SHAVING RASHES

If these happen to you regularly, mix up the following recipe so it's ready when you need it. Fill a 50ml blue or amber bottle with carrier oil. A plain, pure vegetable oil will do, however, if the carrier contains evening primrose oil, peach/apricot kernel oils and/or wheatgerm all the better. Add nine drops Lavender, nine drops chamomile, seven drops cedarwood. Apply after shaving. This blend acts as a moisturizer or, if you prefer, you can wipe off the excess after a few minutes. With the soothing, skin-healing qualities of lavender and chamomile blended with those of cedarwood (one of the first essential oils and used in embalming centuries ago) your skin will never be the same again!

SPRUCE UP THAT BEARD

For those of you with beards who find that your skin gets dry, or if you would just like to pamper yourself, try this blend two to three times a week:

To 50ml of carrier oil, add

cedarwood	8 drops
rosemary	8 drops
lavender	8 drops

Massage into the beard and skin. Leave for a few minutes and wash off in your shower or bath.

SMELLY FEET

Perhaps it is not entirely fair for me to include this information in the men only section, as it is certainly not just a male problem, but, let's face it, guys, I think the numbers of you with smelly feet are greater!

Do check out your diet. Are you consuming at least one litre of water per day? How often do you eat fresh fruit and vegetables? Do you live on fast food? A bad diet, full of the wrong foods, can contribute considerably to smelly feet. I also recommend trying zinc as a mineral supplement for treating long-term foot odour.

Once you have looked at your diet, try essential oils in a foot-bath to combat odour. Fill a large bowl, big enough for both feet. Add two drops of tea tree and two of lemon oil. Soak the feet for a good ten minutes. Try to do this several days in a row – it seems much more effective. Repeat this process every month and it will help to keep the smell at bay!

If you really feel like tackling the problem, try this trick of my grandmother's, too. The mother of several, sporty sons, she had to have a few tricks up her sleeve (as well as a quick sense of humour!). Her recipe was to mix manuka with baking powder, which her sons then used as a foot powder both on their

Make your own foot powder by mixing two to three drops of tea tree oil to every tablespoon of baking powder.

feet and in their shoes. Make your own foot powder by mixing two to three drops of tea tree oil (more available than manuka) to every tablespoon of baking powder. Keep this in an airtight jar, shake before use and dust your feet with it daily, sprinkling a little in your shoes when you are not wearing them.

JOCK ITCH

This is actually caused by a fungus – *Tinea cruris* – and is a real, valid and known condition. The fungus tends to prefer warm, moist habitats and can cause a rather painful rash. Avoid wearing tight clothing in hot weather and pay special attention to keeping the groin area clean and dry. Morning and night, half-fill your basin with water and add two drops of tea tree oil and one drop of lavender (if you have it). Mix the oils into the water, wash the groin area and dry thoroughly. In addition (but not instead of), you could also make up a 10ml bottle of pure vegetable oil with four drops of tea tree oil to apply sparingly to the area as an ointment following the lavender/tea tree wash.

This works really well and, jokes apart, can save you some embarrassment. The same principle can work very effectively for an 'itchy bum' but put four drops of lavender in the carrier oil this time. Make sure you wash the anus twice a day and dry thoroughly, but not roughly, before applying the oil. The relief is tremendous!

PART THREE

Special Occasions

LET'S PARTY!

The mood-enhancing properties of essential oils have been used for centuries. Over the past fifty years, chemicals have reigned and synthetic fragrancing has been more prominent. Perfumery seems to be the only realm in which mood-enhancing essential oils were truly appreciated. Many of us are now aware of the power of aromas to affect our memory. Try using some of your favourite oils and blends to scent the air at your own events and celebrations and make them truly memorable.

CHRISTMAS

Last Christmas I co-ordinated my aromas and the result was wonderful. I love being surprised by oils. Even though I knew the scents well and liked them, when I went out of the house and returned, it was as if the good fairy had been, it was so much nicer than anticipated.

Throughout the year I collected natural plants on my walks: during the summer I found small cones from trees, during the autumn different seeds and pods. I mixed these with cinnamon sticks, dried rosehips and some dried lemon pieces. After adding drops of orange, lemon, cinnamon, nutmeg, clove and ginger essential oils to the pot pourri I sealed the mixture in plastic bags for about a week. When I opened the bags the smell was just gorgeous. For the few weeks prior to Christmas I used the same essential oils in my burners in various blends. I also made up a room spray from orange flower water with the drops of these same Christmas oils. This lovely combination really enhanced my own and visitors' moods.

Another way to imprint your own fragrance on the festive season is by fragrancing your gift-wrapping paper. The oils may make the dye run so drop the oil on the back of the paper. Or store the paper with a fragrant cotton wool ball before using it. Invitations, thank-you notes and Christmas cards may all be fragranced in this way.

EASTER

The essential oils I associate with Easter are cinnamon, lemon, vanilla, *Litsea cubeba* (sometimes called may chang) and geranium. Make your pot pourri a blend of these oils and try a room spray, using five drops of essential oil to about 200ml water. You may like to blend the essential oils first in a little amber bottle and then add five drops of the combination to your spray or pot pourri. Try two drops of geranium, two of *Litsea cubeba* and one of vanilla.

WEDDINGS

For weddings, essential oils of neroli and *Litsea cubeba* are perfect. Neroli is extracted from the flowers of the bitter orange – if you have ever walked through an orange grove when the blossoms are out, this fragrance is something you will never

Neroli is extracted from the flowers of the bitter orange – if you have ever walked through an orange grove when the blossoms are out, this fragrance is something you will never forget.

forget. It is exquisite and probably the most deeply calming of all oils. It seems to have a way of overriding most anxieties. The traditional use of orange blossom in the bridal wreath perhaps had something to do with this. I find neroli has a special kind of purity about it, which we traditionally associate with weddings. This is a lovely oil for the bride to bathe in and wear as a perfume. You could even fragrance the invitations with this aroma. *Litsea cubeba* has a fresh, alive fragrance as well as being antiseptic and deodorizing. It would be good for pot pourri and room sprays at an event such as this. Or try a delicious mixture of petitgrain and *Litsea cubeba*.

DINNER PARTIES

Setting the mood for a dinner party can sometimes be difficult if you've been racing around preparing things. Oils can have a profound effect on these sorts of occasions. Use geranium to encourage a relaxed atmosphere and promote a good feeling;

clary sage is relaxing, encourages conversation and is slightly euphoric. You may like to use a fresher oil, such as lemon or *Litsea cubeba* in part of the dining room. Distribute the fragrance of your oils using sprays, a diffuser or cotton wool balls. Or try a couple of drops of sandalwood or cedarwood essential oils on your firewood before burning. This is lovely for a family party or small dinner party – but is wasted on a crowd! If you have a bowl with floating candles, pop in a couple of drops of essential oil – perhaps using the fresher oils above would be good here. A few minutes spent fragrancing your rooms may make the difference to a whole evening.

ROMANTIC DINNERS

To convey romance try the different kinds of rose, jasmine, ylang-ylang and neroli. They can be supported in blends by geranium, patchouli, lemon and nutmeg. If you want to create a fragrance to use more than once and be recognized by, try out several combinations of these and find a favourite. You could really go to town and fragrance everything, including the tablecloth. I suggest starting with a blend of three drops of ylang-ylang and two of patchouli on your burner. Try a room spray of three drops of jasmine, one drop of nutmeg and two drops of mandarin in 250ml of water. This should be sufficient for dinner. For other ideas, see the section on passion (pages 98–102).

> *To convey romance try the different kinds of rose, jasmine, ylang-ylang and neroli.*

PARTIES

Experiment with more stimulating oils when you have a party. Choose from ginger, black pepper, mandarin, grapefruit, orange and coriander. Again try out all the different ways you can think of to fragrance your environment. You could even try putting essential oils onto a cotton wool ball and popping it in the cardboard of the toilet roll holder. Or throw a few drops of your old essential oils down the toilet. Nowhere need be exempt from your fragrances!

If colds and flu are about you may like to choose a practical antibacterial party aroma. Choose from lemon, geranium, pine, clove, lavender, clary sage and bergamot. All of these oils are uplifting.

CLEARING YOUR SPACE

After a party your environment may feel a little battered. Clearing your space is very important. Open as many windows as possible, clean the rooms as usual, and then re-fragrance them with three drops of lavender and two drops of bergamot on a burner. Or try three drops of pine, two of mandarin and one of *Litsea cubeba* in 200ml of water as a room spray.

Then take yourself off to be cleansed too. Sometimes we don't give this enough importance, but being around a lot of people drains the system, whether you feel it or not. Fill your bath and try adding two drops of juniper and three drops of grapefruit. This is also a great bath if you feel you've just had enough! It is very restorative.

> *Being around a lot of people drains the system, whether you feel it or not*

PASSIONATE MOMENTS

This aspect of life will always hold a fascination for us. Essential oils with aphrodisiac qualities have an indefinable mystique. They capture the imagination in a way that only an aroma can.

If you've never experimented with these kinds of oils before, you could begin using them in your own skincare. All the aphrodisiac oils are great for your skin. Like perfume, each of them smells quite different from one body to the next.

Fragrances for her:
Rose, neroli, jasmine and ylang-ylang are all beautiful fragrances for a woman. Try them in the bath, as individual oils or combine two together. Try one or two drops in a teaspoon of pure vegetable oil (try peach or apricot kernel) and use as a face or body oil. To begin with try some of these oils just on their own. They all have quite different 'personalities' and it's fun to get to know them.

Fragrances for him:
Sandalwood, ylang-ylang, vetiver or clary sage are all wonderful fragrances for men. Jasmine is a scent for both sexes, as it has both masculine and feminine aspects, and it can be wonderful on some men.

> *Sandalwood, ylang-ylang, vetiver or clary sage are all wonderful fragrances for men.*

The aphrodisiac oils tend to be the most expensive ones. Here is a little background on the most affordable one:

YLANG-YLANG

Ylang-ylang (*Cananga odorata*) is a small tree which grows in Indonesia, the Philippines and Madagascar. Ylang-ylang means 'flower of flowers' and you can find pink-, mauve- and yellow-flowered varieties. The best oil comes from the yellow flowers, which are picked very early in the day, in early summer. The oil is produced by steam distillation. The flowers may be distilled several times, and the oil varies in quality, depending on the distillation. The first distillation and the finest oil is known as 'extra'. Only this 'extra' has the required properties for therapeutic use.

The chemical constituents of ylang-ylang are many and varied. They include methyl benzoate, methyl salicilate, geraniol, linalol, eugenol, ylangol, terpenes safrol, benzyl acetate and pinene. It also contains a combination of benzoic, salicylic, formic, acetic and valeric acids.

The most important property of Ylang-ylang is its ability to slow down rapid breathing and rapid heart rate. In shock and trauma situations this is one of the oils to reach for. Anyone with a long-term condition such as this should of course be under professional guidance for their treatment.

Ylang-ylang is good for any skin as it balances the natural oil production. Its sweet, heavy, distinctive fragrance is used widely in perfumes and cosmetics. Like the three major aphrodisiac oils – rose, neroli and jasmine – ylang-ylang is beautifully uplifting emotionally and very relaxing. The calming effect of this oil may be the reason it is considered an aphrodisiac. Using it would definitely lessen tensions or anxieties involving sexual matters.

CREATING THE MOOD

The ancient Romans traditionally covered the marriage bed with rose petals. They would dress the bride in a headdress adorned with orange blossom flowers. Rose and neroli are renowned for calming anxieties and nervousness.

Start your own traditions! Try cotton wool balls with jasmine or ylang-ylang in your lingerie drawer. Or, for him, sandalwood to scent underwear.

We all like different aromas, so try out combinations of the oils to find your favourite. What you like as a room spray may not be the same as what you like to put in your diffuser. The combination for massage may be

> **The ancient Romans traditionally covered the marriage bed with rose petals.**

quite different from what you like in the bath. Experiment with different combinations. If you aren't sure where to start, here are some suggestions:

Aphrodisiacs for the bath:

Love potion: Rose, neroli and jasmine – one drop of each of these in two teaspoons of apricot kernel oil makes a totally luxurious and aphrodisiac bath. If this is too feminine, try two drops of sandalwood and three of ylang-ylang in two teaspoons of base oil for a more 'unisex' fragrance.

For a pick-me-up, yet aphrodisiac, bath: try two drops of ylang-ylang and three drops of grapefruit in two teaspoons of base oil.

Love potion massage:

Exchanging massage can be a beautifully sensual part of love-making. The simplest and one of the best combinations is two drops of ylang-ylang and one drop of sandalwood in two teaspoons of base oil.

> *As well as being aphrodisiac this blend will leave your skin feeling truly wonderful*

As well as being aphrodisiac this blend will leave your skin feeling truly wonderful – I call it 'skin food'. Essential oils may irritate the delicate skin of the genital area so do take care.

Love potion spray:

In 200ml of water try two drops of jasmine, one drop of nutmeg, one drop of black pepper and one drop of citrus (lemon, grapefruit or *Litsea cubeba*). Spray this in the bedroom. Take care to avoid delicate fabrics, but try a little spray on the curtains, cushions, carpet, and bed clothes. Or try a little on cotton wool balls and sit these on the radiator. This blend will be a refreshing, uplifting aphrodisiac aroma.

Love potions to diffuse:

Try each of the oils on their own at some point. Then try the ones you 'feel' would go together – like flavours when you're cooking. Exercise that intuition. A drop of clary sage may be nice every now and then. People either love or hate patchouli, but you could try a drop of this too sometimes. The citrus oils will lighten the heavier aromas – grapefruit goes well with ylang-ylang, lemon with sandalwood. Discover your own combinations.

Angel water:

In the eighteenth century, a special 'potion' was presented to a couple on their wedding day to send them on their merry way. An old English recipe for this would have probably included rose water, myrtle water, some distilled spirit of musk and a dash of ambergris.

Although these ingredients are not what we would use today, I think this idea is lovely. You may like to create your own 'angel blend' when you have found your favourite oils. Then you will have a smell to call your own.

After all this talk of love potions, you may need cooling down! If you need something to dampen lust, try marjoram. Although, as Ovid wrote: 'But alas! There are no herbs to cure love', majoram does come close. It is said to 'ease sexual excitement' and has been used in religious institutions over the centuries as it 'lessens the emotional response and the physical sensation'. Try it if an antidote to all the aphrodisiacs is needed!

> *If you need something to dampen lust, try marjoram.*

CONFIDENCE BOOSTERS

Confidence can sometimes be elusive. Others may try to convince you that you have every reason to be confident, and you may try to convince yourself, yet somehow at times it is just not there.

If you watch young children, their confidence generally seems to come from a physical source. If they can move about comfortably in their bodies, easy in their environment, they seem to have confidence in everything. But by the time some of us reach adulthood, it can feel as though confidence is non-existent. For me, like many others, gaining confidence has seemed like a huge mountain to climb. When I was finally able to pronounce myself 'confident', I was devastated to find it wasn't for ever. Even now that I've reached the top of my mountain, I still have periods in my life when my confidence just vanishes. It can take so much internal work to find it again. Just using oils as part of your life helps. I think this is because they bring you more in touch with your own body. One oil in particular has helped me tremendously. Perhaps it was just the right oil at the right time for me, but I know it has been important to others as well. That oil is jasmine.

JASMINE

Jasmine (*Jasmine officinalis*) is a wonderful yin/yang mix. When you look up jasmine in reference books, you find that some categorize it as masculine, while others claim it to be feminine. I think it holds both aspects beautifully. The flowers are delicate and feminine. The oil is thick and dark and the aroma has an almost earthy undertone.

Jasmine is harvested in France, Egypt and India. The main chemical components are indol, benzyl alcohol, benzyl acetate, linalol, methyl anthranilate and linalyl acetate. The properties of jasmine are very like those of rose and, like rose, jasmine oil has never successfully been synthesized. It is helpful for many 'feminine' problems and is a valuable uterine tonic. It can help to ease pain in the early stage of labour if massaged into the lower back and abdomen and will also strengthen contractions. It's a lovely oil to use after you've given birth as it has a strong anti-depressant action. Jasmine is equally valuable in helping with 'masculine' problems and may assist with prostate trouble. It is also said to strengthen the male sex organs!

For centuries, jasmine has been regarded as an aphrodisiac and can be helpful with sexual problems. Warming and relaxing, jasmine is a lovely oil for massage. These qualities extend to the emotional and mental planes also. This is where jasmine gets its reputation for being an uplifting oil, an antidepressant and stress reliever.

Small amounts of jasmine are wonderful in skincare too, especially for dry, sensitive skins. And of course it is well loved for its beautiful aroma.

It can help to ease pain in the early stage of labour if massaged into the lower back and abdomen and will also strengthen contractions.

From my experience, jasmine has a special way of enabling femininity to manifest itself physically. It seems to help increase confidence in your own physicality and strengthens your self-belief.

- Try bathing in a jasmine bath once a week.
- Burn the oil while you are working, a couple of times a week.
- Mix two drops of jasmine in a teaspoon of base oil and wear it as a perfume.

Jasmine can be a beautiful tool, enjoy it!

Certain oils are natural confidence boosters. They work through our sense of smell, on the limbic system in the brain. Jasmine is one of these. Other oils that help build confidence are petit-grain, lemon, bergamot, melissa and neroli. Try the following blend:

To 50ml of carrier oil add:

neroli	8 drops
petitgrain	6 drops
jasmine	8 drops
lemon	3 drops

You can add this oil to your bath, use it as a body oil or wear it on your pulse points during the day, like a perfume. There may be other blends you prefer. Try this first and gradually alter the mix to suit you.

SHEER INDULGENCE

I am often asked what my best-loved oils and bath blends are. Here are some of my favourites – some practical, some indulgent.

NEROLI, PETITGRAIN AND ORANGE

These three exquisite oils are extracted from different parts of the same tree. Orange is from the fruit, petitgrain from the leaves and small twigs and neroli from the actual orange blossom flowers. Perhaps it is because they all come from the same source, but when these three are combined they create a whole fragrance that is more uplifting, relaxing, soothing and warming than each of them individually or any other blend. It is one of my all-time favourites – sheer heaven.

FRANKINCENSE AND GRAPEFRUIT

Sometimes there is something in me that craves this bath. It is usually only when I am in it that I realize there is a reason I need it. While I'm soaking, I'll reflect on the past few days and become aware that I need to let go of a way of

Frankincense is wonderful for liberating you from the past.

thinking, a perception or an attitude. Frankincense is wonderful for liberating you from the past. As well as having this effect on the psyche, frankincense and grapefruit are a beautiful combination both to fragrance your rooms and bathe in.

JUNIPER AND GRAPEFRUIT

This is a 'saviour' bath. When others have demanded too much of you, when you are 'peopled' out, and you just want to scream, this is the bath for you. The grapefruit is beautifully uplifting, mentally and emotionally. It will re-energize you. Juniper eliminates waste from the parts of the body on which it is used. It seems to clear away the debris from the mind, too, just as effectively. I call this the 'mum's mix' as mothers can have so many demands made on them. If you're a mother, remember this one.

> *When others have demanded too much of you, when you are 'peopled' out, and you just want to scream, this is the bath for you.*

LAVENDER AND BERGAMOT

This blend was possibly the first I ever attempted. Now I cannot remember life without lavender. It has transformational powers in a bath – something that I need regularly! Add to those relaxing, restorative powers of lavender just a touch of bergamot. Although uplifting, bergamot does not detract in any way from

> *When I am tired, I often feel a bit down. I find bergamot lifts my spirits and I sleep even better.*

the relaxing effect of the lavender. When I am tired, I often feel a bit down. I find bergamot lifts my spirits and I sleep even better. I would whole-heartedly recommend this bath to everyone.

JUST JASMINE

There is something about jasmine that I seem to be drawn to every now and then. I feel very regal and feminine bathing in jasmine. It is a beautifully pampering bath, very relaxing and restorative. Jasmine is the one oil I use often on its own. A good Jasmine oil is an exquisite thing – it feels like a blend. Try this bath and see what you think.

VETIVER, CHAMOMILE AND LEMON

I seriously do not know how I would have survived without this bath. It's for when you're so stressed you feel like a zombie with a fuzzy brain and you know your mind just won't stop. If this sounds like you, run yourself one of these baths. You will sleep like a baby and wake up with a brain that has potential!

Vetiver is marvellous for stress, chamomile helps that irritable feeling and really soothes and the lemon is rejuvenating and fortifies the nervous system. This is not an everyday bath, but once or twice in a stressful week it is a life saver.

APHRODITE'S BATH

Instead of mixing your favourite oils just in a base oil, try blending them in a cup of whole milk and adding that to the bath. I always add a little base oil as well, then the whole bath becomes luxuriously moisturizing, milky and fragrant. When you think of it, that's what queens, princesses and Aphrodite, the Greek goddess of love and beauty, would have bathed in. I'm sure she couldn't have had ass's milk every bath! It's a lovely change and it does feel gorgeous on the skin.

BEAUTY SPECIALS

One of the wonderful things about using essential oils for face and body treatments is that you are always enhancing the 'inner' aspects of beauty while you are treating the outer ones.

As we go through life our beauty needs change. They alter with fashion, how much time and money we have, our age and stage of life. I am always happy to try new ideas for beauty treatments, but I always miss my oils. None of the commercial products I have ever used has given me more pleasure or felt so good on my skin as oils. I find myself constantly disappointed with new products that look lovely, seem a good idea but are made synthetically.

> *As natural ingredients are becoming more available, it is now quite simple to make your own products or find someone locally who does.*

Every culture has always had its own products made from seasonal, local produce. Using, as far as possible, plants and vegetables that are in season in your area seems healthy and 'right'. As natural ingredients are becoming more available, it is now quite simple to make your own products or find someone locally who does. Why use a cream that has chemicals and preservatives when you can use something natural that's even better?

There are now some lovely books available on making your own cosmetics, so here I will just outline an idea of the oils you might like to use in your homemade preparations. These recipes are just examples to start you off. Go ahead and create!

FOR THE FACE

Tonics
Tonics stimulate the circulation, balance the natural oils and help close open pores. One of the simplest and loveliest is

rosewater. This is the water which remains after the essential oil has been extracted from rose petals.

You can make your own tonic water by heating 100ml distilled or spring water. While this is still quite warm add up to about five drops of your preferred essential oils. Choose from:

Sensitive skins – one drop of Roman chamomile (lovely if you use chamomile water as well)
Normal/dry skins – one drop each of rose and sandalwood oils
Normal/oily skin – one drop each of neroli and orange oils.
Blemishes – one drop each of lavender and juniper oils (see Spot treatment section, page 51).

Pour your mix into a bottle. Leave for twenty-four hours then strain it through an unbleached coffee filter and back into your bottle. Shake well before using.

Oils
Essential oils penetrate deeply through *all* the layers of the skin. With the increased circulation they create, they will help to bring oxygen and nutrients to the skin. Generally they will improve the quality of the skin – and it feels better from the inside too. You can add your essential oils to natural, additive-free creams and lotions and to any natural face masks that you like.

Base oils
Try almond, apricot kernel and peach kernel. Use these in any combination, or on their own, and make your base oil up to 30ml by adding 2ml borage seed oil and 2ml vitamin E oil for a truly nourishing blend.
Then choose from:

Normal skin: chamomile, geranium, lavender, rose, lemon, jasmine, neroli. For this skin type add up to fifteen drops of the oils that you like to the base oil. Every time you mix your oils you can try a slightly different recipe.
Dryish skin: you may like to add a little avocado oil or wheatgerm oil to your base oil. These are both lovely moisturizers.

For 30ml base oil choose fifteen drops taken from lavender, chamomile, sandalwood, rose, benzoin, geranium, rosemary, neroli. **Oily skin:** choose your fifteen drops from chamomile, lavender, juniper, geranium, lemon, rosemary, jasmine, ylang-ylang, frank-incense and petitgrain.

Here is an example of a recipe or two to get you on the right track:

For younger skin:		*For more mature skin:*	
Base:		Base:	
almond oil	20ml	almond oil	10ml
apricot kernel	10ml	apricot kernel	5ml
		peach kernel	5ml
		wheatgerm	5ml
Add		borage seed and	
lavender	4 drops	vitamin E	5ml
chamomile	3 drops		
geranium	3 drops	Add:	
lemon	1 drop	rose	3 drops
rose	2 drops	neroli	3 drops
rosemary	1 drop	jasmine	2 drops
neroli	1 drop	frankincense	2 drops
		myrrh	2 drops
		lemon	1 drop
		lavender	2 drops

Try either of these blends as a neck oil too – I always try to include my neck as part of my daily beauty routine – it can easily get forgotten!

One of the most exquisite ways to use oils is in these face treatments, as the aromas are with you all day, every day. They will benefit your psyche at the same time as your skin. You just can't lose!

HAIR

Essential oils will not alter the colour of your hair. They can, however, help to keep it healthy and enhance the colour.

It is relatively easy to make your own shampoo. You can make a 'base' shampoo using pure soap flakes and spring water. Just 100g of flakes to one litre of water. Seal and store this in your fridge. Then mix your shampoo as you need it. Choose from the following:

Normal hair: put 100ml of your soap base in the blender with five drops of borage oil, two drops of rosemary, three drops of lemon and three of geranium. Use as ordinary shampoo.

Dry hair: to 100ml of base, add two drops of sandalwood and three of geranium along with one teaspoon jojoba oil and one teaspoon apricot kernel oil.

Oily hair: blend three drops of lavender, five of lemon and four of eucalyptus with 100ml of soap base.

Alternatively, you could buy a very mild, non-perfumed shampoo and add these blends. Either would be preferable to some of the harsh, chemical shampoos on the market.

Rinses

Make an infusion of real fresh or dried herbs. You can boost this with a couple of drops of a complementary essential oil.

The basic infusion Take a large handful of the fresh leaves or about 25g of the dried herb of your choice. Add this to about 1.2 litres water in a saucepan. Bring to the boil and simmer for about ten minutes. Leave to cool for two hours, then strain off the water to use.

Fair hair: use chamomile flowers for your basic infusion. Warm the water to use in the rinse. Pour into a large bowl. After washing, rinse the hair several times and leave on for about twenty minutes. Do your final rinse with ordinary water.

Dark hair: substitute sage leaves for the chamomile flowers above and follow the same sequence.

> ***For a classic rinse:*** this is an alternative to the classic beer rinse: add 50ml of leftover, flat beer to 50ml of pure water, mix with two teaspoons cider vinegar, three drops of rosemary and three drops of lemon essential oils.

Tonics

Rosemary: make an infusion, as above, with fresh rosemary and add a couple of drops of rosemary essential oil. Use this as a basic infusion rinse.

Nettle: this is a lovely tonic and can help to clear dandruff. *Carefully* collect your nettles – grab them boldly to avoid getting stung – or even better, wear gloves! Add a good handful to a pint of water and heat slowly. Cover and simmer only for about five minutes. Leave to stand and cool for two hours. Then use as the basic infusion, as above.

Hair loss

There can be many reasons for hair loss. If you begin to lose hair drastically, see your doctor and take a serious look at your general state of health. There are times when we just lose more hair than usual. Essential oils can stimulate the hair follicles, restore balance to sebum production and increase the circulation and oxidization, which can sometimes help regrowth. Try this recipe:

Base:	jojoba oil	45ml
	borage seed oil	5ml
Add:	rosemary	10 drops
	lemon	5 drops
	lavender	5 drops
	cedarwood	5 drops

Massage this mixture into your scalp and, if you can, leave it overnight, wrapped in cling film and cover your pillow with an old towel. Shampoo as usual in the morning.

EYES

Throughout Europe the herb 'eyebright' is considered the best natural remedy for the eyes. The Germans call this 'consolation for the eyes', to the Italians it is 'luminella' while the French call it 'casse-lunette' – they anticipate you throw away your glasses after using this!

For tired, strained eyes there is nothing quite as good as cucumber. Grate a little, put in some gauze and rest with these little packs over the eyes for ten minutes.

Essential oils come into their own for the skin around the eyes. The following oils are lovely for around the eye area. As base oils: hazelnut oil, almond oil, apricot kernel oil, peach kernel oil, borage seed oil, vitamin E oil. To these add the following essential oils: lavender, neroli, rose, chamomile or fennel.

Here are some suggested recipes to get you going:

For younger skin:		*For more mature skin*:	
Base:		Base:	
apricot kernel oil	5 ml	apricot kernel oil	5ml
peach kernel oil	5 ml	hazelnut oil	5 ml
vitamin E	2 capsules or 1ml of oil	vitamin E	2 capsules or 2ml of oil
borage seed	2 drops	borage seed	5 drops
Add:		Add:	
lavender	2 drops	lavender	1 drop
chamomile	1 drop	neroli	1 drop
		rose	1 drop

Note that when applying oil to the eyes take care not to get them in the eyes. Apply to the skin very lightly in tiny amounts (tissue off after five minutes if you like) and do not apply to the eyelid. Use every night.

HANDS

If you have a favourite hand cream try adding ten drops of your preferred essential oils from the following list: to each 50g of cream add lemon, lavender, lime, eucalyptus. All these are good antiseptics. Or, alternatively, try patchouli, geranium, sandalwood, rose, benzoin. These are all excellent moisturizers.

My favourite recipe is four drops of lavender, four of lemon and four of benzoin. This is marvellous for dry and cracked hands as well as feet.

If you prefer a lotion for your hands try this old English recipe: to 100ml of rose water and 50ml of glycerine add ten drops of lavender, plus a squeeze of lemon juice for good measure.

NAILS

Years ago I made a face oil for a friend of mine who was a trained beautician. She really enjoyed using it, but was far more impressed with the effect if had on her nails! Regularly working with oils strengthens and conditions the fingernails as if by magic. And this is only one of the lovely side-effects! Specifically for strong healthy nails try this recipe for daily use:

Base:	jojoba oil	5 ml
	apricot kernel	5 ml
	borage seed	2 drops
Add:	rosemary	2 drops
	lavender	3 drops
	lemon	3 drops

LIPS

Find yourself a chemical-free pot of lip balm. Place this dish inside a pot with a small amount of water in it. Heat gently until the balm has softened. Then add four drops of lavender and four drops of geranium essential oil (or rose or chamomile). Leave to cool. For those who would like to make their own lip balm, try 25g of beeswax, 1ml of vitamin E oil and about ten drops of jojoba oil. Melt all the ingredients in the same way as above and add your preferred essential oils.

For coldsores, add one drop of lavender and one drop of tea tree to a cottonbud and apply directly to the affected area. Some people find that tea tree alone is good. However, it can be drying so always use your lip salve afterwards to keep lips moist.

> *For coldsores, add one drop of lavender and one drop of tea tree to a cottonbud and apply directly to the affected area.*

TEETH AND GUMS

Many cultures have different traditions for keeping teeth healthy. From charcoal and rock salt, to chewing betel leaves, burnt ground hazelnuts, soft willow twigs or strawberries. We now have toothpaste and dental floss to fight sugar with. For a general mouthwash to back up your other mouthcare try two drops of tea tree oil, two drops of lemon and one of peppermint in 200ml of still spring water. For gum problems, just add one drop of myrrh. Keep in a brown bottle and rinse (and gargle if you want to) twice a day.

For beauty treatments for your feet see the Treat the Feet section, pages 79–82. For cellulite see the Detox section, pages 39–43.

PART FOUR

The Last Word

THE ELEMENTS

As colours are the basic elements of creating a *visual* picture, essential oils are the elements for creating *aroma* pictures. They can be helpful to counter bacteria, lift our moods, feed our skin and yet they can also give us access to a whole 'other world' with the *aroma* pictures they can create. I love this side of working with oils. Smells are so evocative.

Using the basic elements, essential oils, I decided to look at the elements: earth, air, fire and water. The *feel* of each element has been matched to the oils that feel nearest. I've then created a couple of aroma pictures relating to each element.

EARTH

Everything about the element earth is indeed earthy. Grounded, strong, tree-like, stable, balanced, steadfast.

The oils that are most like this element are, naturally enough, derived from trees and woods, and their roots and resins. Examples are benzoin, cedarwood, frankincense, myrrh, petit-grain, pine, rosewood, sandalwood and vetiver. All the earth oils have rather earthy aromas and are relaxing and warming.

Fresh Forest: cedarwood, pine and lime. This is a lovely blend is lovely to burn or diffuse. Alternatively, pop some on cottonwool balls and place these on radiators around the house. And try it in the sauna.

The Bush: cedarwood, benzoin, vertivert and petitgrain.
I was brought up walking in the bush and didn't realize that nowhere else in the world smells like the New Zealand bush. Damp and fresh with an earthy fragrance.

AIR

The element air always seems to be associated with the intellect and mental energy: the sharp, mental ability to cut through the air and find the important things. It is the element of perception and reason.

The oils that seem to connect instantly with this element are: lemon, peppermint, rosemary, kanuka and bergamot. All the air oils are stimulating, refreshing and uplifting.

Sunrise and Sunset: lemon, rosemary and clary sage.
The ancient Egyptians believed that these twilight times were important. It was at these times, when the sky was turquoise and indigo, that the invisible became visible. Fresh, chilly, very clear and slightly 'other worldly'.

Autumn Breeze: kanuka, bergamot and benzoin.
Takes away the inner 'cobwebs' and gets the lungs breathing deeply again. Kanuka is 'white' tea tree, a sister species of manuka and Australian tea tree. This blend makes you glad to be alive.

FIRE

This element holds the human warmth. This needs to ignite every now and then into the flames of passion, zest and drive. The oils of fire, energy and dynamism are lemon, grapefruit, ginger, coriander, orange, black pepper and nutmeg.

Zest: lemon, orange and grapefruit. Uplifting, rejuvenating and mentally refreshing.

Drive: lemon, sandalwood and basil. This blend will assist you in your search to find your inner resources of power, focus and clarity.

Hearth of the Home: ginger, orange and patchouli. The warmth, relaxation and wonderful feeling of snuggling in front of the fire.

WATER

The element of water is symbolic of our flowing life force. Very physical, yet feminine. Very powerful, yet soft. Enormously destructive, yet the key to all life. Water seems to be both masculine and feminine.

One oil relates instantly to water. When you describe jasmine you could so often be describing water. The water oils are rose, jasmine, neroli, clary sage and juniper. All these oils relate to creativity somehow. They are all aphrodisiacs!

Under a Waterfall: geranium, juniper and grapefruit.
The mood under a waterfall is exhilarating. A strong mental and emotional shift upwards and a divine feeling of being cleansed outside and inside.

Deep Bottomless Pool: clary sage, neroli and sandalwood. Sandalwood provides depth and strength, neroli the connection with the divine and the clary sage just carries you into the pool.

For a healthy, balanced human being we should, according to Chinese wisdom, have all these four elements fluctuating equally through our lives.

For me, meditation is walking or doing the dishes. The nearest I get to the classic meditation is taking a deliciously long bath, lighting lots of candles, having a wallow and a sip or two of wine! Creating *aroma* pictures for these baths is one of my treats, for I just do not know what I'll discover at Sunrise or in a Deep Bottomless Pool.